A BRIDGE TO

Donald Bailey, aged 46, as he was in the immediate post-war years. This photograph was taken during his visit to the USA. *Bailey Archives*.

Ministry of Defence
Directorate of Engineer Services (Army)

A Bridge to Victory

The Untold Story of the Bailey Bridge

Brian Harpur

Foreword by Sir Colin Cole KCVO TD FSA

London: HMSO

Front cover illustration
A painting by T. Cuneo of the Royal Engineers bridging the River Rapido at Cassino, Italy, on the night of 12/13 May 1944. During this action, 15 sappers were killed and 57, including three officers, were wounded. *Reproduced by kind permission of the Officers of the Corps of Royal Engineers.*)

Printed in the UK for HMSO
Dd 0293525 11.91 C20 531/3 12521

Contents

Acknowledgements

FOR constant assistance, encouragement, and for supplying valuable archive material, references, and information I am particularly indebted to Lady Bailey, Richard Bailey, and Sir Ralph Freeman. I am also grateful to Brigadier S. A. Stewart and Brigadier H. A. T. Jarrett-Kerr and other officers of the Corps of Royal Engineers who gave me the authentic details of the origin and development of Sir Donald Bailey's idea, and who, with Sir Ralph Freeman, helped to make valuable suggestions about parts of the typescript. I also wish to thank the following for their contributions, all of which are included in essence in the book.

Mr Edward Aubury
Lt Col. G. D. Bailey
Mrs S. Bailey
Mrs Leland Batchelder
Mr B. T. Bellis
Mr T. C. Bickerton
Mr C. A. Bramwell
Mr Martin Bridle
Mrs Lorna Carey
Lt M. Cheman
Mr T. K. Clifford
Captain Teddy Cullen
Mr G. Davis
Sir Frederick Dainton
Mr M. A. Davidson
Mr E. S. Davies

Mrs C. Dayman
Mr D. M. Delany
Mr W. A. B. Douglas
Mrs D. Dowsett
Mr J. W. Dunn
Mr B. A. Fireman
Mr Charles Forsyth
Mr R. A. Foulkes
Colonel J. H. Frankeau
Major Chris J. Grant
Miss Liliane Grantham
Mrs P. Gwenllian
Mr John Hancock
Mr A. W. Hanlon
Mr Gordon Hardy
Major J. A. E. Hathrell

Mr A. G. Harvey
Mr C. Hill
Lt Col. G. A. Hills
Imperial War Museum
Institution of Royal Engineers
Lt Col. T. H. Jermyn
Mr M. Johnston
Colonel J. H. Joiner
Mr C. J. Kenyon
Mrs M. Kerley
Mrs Elsie Labrum
Mrs Jane Long
Mr H. McGhee
Mr Bevil Mabey
Mr N. Marner
Metal Construction Magazine
Mr H. Miners
Colonel G. W. A. Napier
Colonel Kenneth H. Osborne
Lt M. H. Patriquin
Mr William S. Pickworth
Mr Bill Rawling
Mrs G. Anne Robertson
Mr John Royle
Royal Armament Research and

Development Establishment
Mr J. W. Scott
Major W. H. Scott
Mr John J. Slonaker
Professor G. D. Sims
Mr C. Leslie Smith
Mrs Lily Smith
Dr Richard Smith
Captain John Stevenson
Mr J. Stirland
Major N. E. Thackeray
Professor C. J. Tranter
Mr Ion Trewin
Major General A. Trythall
Mr Jeremy Wallington
Lt Gen. G. Walsh
Brigadier H. B. C. Watkins
Mrs Constance Watts
Mr A. Whitehouse
Mr G. H. Wilkins
Mr John Williams
Miss Jane With
Mr Stephen Wragg
Mr T. A. Wright

Finally special thanks to my friend Mr Laurence Cotterell for his guidance and particularly to my wife Mimi for assisting in my researches and checking my drafts.

Sources of Illustrations

I am grateful to the following for permission to reproduce the photographs and illustrations included in this book:

Bailey Archive

British Aerospace

Imperial War Museum

Institution of Royal Engineers

Littlewoods

Mabey & Johnson

Saatchi & Saatchi

Thomas Storey (Engineers) Ltd

Preface

THE subject of this book is a man whose story has never been told. His name, when first revealed to the British public mid-way through World War II, was Donald Bailey and as any telephone directory will reveal, there are thousands of Baileys all over the world. But this Mr Bailey was unique.

Destined to join the ranks of anonymous Civil Servants, he might have remained in obscurity to this day but for the fact that he became the subject of many questions regarding his identity. These were prompted by the growing curiosity of the Allied armies who wanted to find out more about their mysterious benefactor whose name had been associated with equipment they had never seen before but found so vital for victory. 'The outstanding marvel of the war' as one newspaper claimed later.

It must be borne in mind by those who have the academic degrees, skills, and experience in the scientific field in which Donald Bailey operated, that I have written this book in terms which I hope every layman can understand. They will forgive, I hope, my over-simplifying matters which they would handle with the minutiae of technical reference.

I wrote this book with humility as a heartfelt tribute both to Donald Bailey and to those whose blood, toil, and tears made it possible for his invention to be so brilliantly exploited in pursuit of victory in a manner which it alone made possible.

BRIAN HARPUR

Foreword

IT is remarkable how chance can affect one's life, or prompt an undertaking of an unexpected kind. A casual meeting with a former Royal Engineer officer in 1980 led Brian Harpur to recall his own experience in battle of the Bailey Bridge, described in compelling detail in Chapter 2 of this book, 'The Trauma of Termoli'. He was driven to investigate and finally to set down in print the story of this great invention and to pay tribute to the vital part which Donald Bailey and his small team played in winning the Second World War.

Until *A Bridge to Victory* no single work has concerned itself with the Bailey Bridge. Even during the second half of the War it was often taken for granted, to the extent that the soldier was more likely to grumble about its absence than to realize at what cost it had been put in place, or how crucial it was tactically to the Allies as they fought their way forward against determined opposition. There is no doubt however that if he knew that a Bailey Bridge had been or was going to be laid across the obstacles ahead, a general uplifting of morale resulted.

As a Troop Commander in a tank battalion I remember very well how if a tank bridge-layer could not do the job, a Bailey Bridge would: it was often the only means of overcoming especially difficult terrain to keep tanks and troops moving instead of becoming pinned down by enemy fire. The following extract from the history of the 6th Guards Tank Brigade, dealing with the final battles between the Weser and Elbe, is typical of the way in which, with tanks and Royal Engineers tasked together, a Bailey Bridge would be called for, and evidence also of the hazards that could attend such an operation. The tanks 'brushed aside some bazooka and small arms opposition, only to meet another very large crater a mile and a half beyond. This was very cleverly sited with a bog on either side and was quite out of the question for a bridge layer. So it was decided to build a Bailey Bridge over it. But while the Sappers were starting work, a time-bomb, of which there were several buried in the side of the road, went off killing some of the Engineers and wounding Lieutenant Gordon, Sergeant Aitken and Guardsman Wally.'

Donald Bailey was well aware of the heroic role of the Sappers in handling the equipment that he had designed to ease their task, and I am sure that he would have regarded this book, as intended by its author, not only as a tribute to the Bailey Bridge as a piece of military hardware but also as an acknowledgement of the courage and endurance of the Royal Engineers as, in every theatre of war, they constructed the bridges named after him.

To Brian Harpur, who died before his book was published, I would pay my own tribute, and count it a privilege to do so, by saying that he undertook a noble task in portraying an ingenious and resolute man, Sir Donald Bailey, and that he has well and truly erected a memorial to Sir Donald, his Bailey Bridges, and those who used them so effectively in wartime, as also to those many engineers since who in peace have built bridges all over the world modelled on his original creation.

July 1991

1 The Envelope

ON a stormy night in late 1940, the drawing office staff at the Experimental Bridging Establishment (EBE) at Christchurch, Hampshire, were working late. They had no idea they were about to learn of a secret project that was going to pave the way to victory in the Allied struggle against Nazi Germany. Sitting with heads bent over their desks and drawing boards, they were dimly aware that the melancholy moan of the wind outside accurately reflected the mood of the nation.

In 1940 Britain stood alone against the might of Hitler's air force and armies. The debacle and miracle of Dunkirk, the repulse of the enemy in the skies in September, the gaining of time to strengthen defences, had all been achieved. Yet there was this sad aching thought that there could be no end to the war. Bombs were still blasting London and other British cities. Fresh in their minds was the savage destruction of Coventry, in the heart of England, on 14 November 1940. Wave after wave of German aircraft dropped 40,000 fire bombs and 500 tons of high explosive which saturated the city indiscriminately. Many thousands of civilian casualties resulted which, together with miles of smoking debris and the moans of many buried alive, created a picture of unprecedented horror.

It is worth recalling that the German codename for this murderous mission was 'Moonlight Sonata'. Somehow it is not surprising that the Nazis, who consigned great books to the bonfire in Berlin, should use the title of Beethoven's music to orchestrate a cacophony of death. Furthermore, relishing the awful destruction which they had made, the Nazi hierarchy introduced as part of their propaganda a new English word. It was to 'Coventrate', meaning to reduce totally to rubble a large urban area by random bombing.

1

It was also a time when countless lives and ships carrying aid to Britain were lost as the German submarine packs took their toll. The population was being put on increasingly short rations. There seemed little hope of averting a war of such attrition. Even if stalemate could be achieved, the nation would be in just as parlous a state as that of defeat itself.

The prospect was as grey and colourless as the drab camouflage paint in widespread use. The only thing to do was to take each day as it came and breathe a sigh of relief when that day came and went without any particular mishap. This was the philosophy of the drawing office staff as late that night they struggled with the modifications to a bridge which had first been used over 20 years before in World War I.

There was desultory banter and conversation as they pored over the blueprints in a routine and somewhat boring task. There was nothing to signal that this would be anything but the same monotonous pattern of tiresome duty and fatigue which characterized previous days. But then, when least expected, as fate so often decides, their whole world was transformed. Something happened which rocked the Establishment then, and for years to come.

In the words of a certain Miss Elvin, then aged 16, who was assisting with the drawings at that time 'Suddenly Mr Bailey, our chief design officer, burst into the room. He was waving an envelope on which he had drawn a sketch and said "This is going to take us into Germany!" ' The utterance was not only electrifying; it became true.

THE STORY now moves back to events earlier that same day. The dark winter evening matched the gloomy mood of two army officers and a civilian leaving Cambridge by car. There was at first little conversation as they proceeded on their melancholy journey. They were distressed. The awful implications of a crucial testing of a trusty old bridge now much modified lay heavily upon them. While the test had not exactly been a failure, they realized that it was at best a patched-up solution imposed on a structure that was already difficult to handle and to launch. But more important, it could only be made by relatively few specialist firms, thus inhibiting the mass production of the components which would soon be desperately required. They had prayed that this revised version would be good enough to carry the vastly heavier tanks of the future, and go into immediate production as standard military equipment. Instead they concluded that no way could this become the all-purpose bridge which the army needed.

Now both they and their expectations were shattered. All seemed lost. Nothing was left except a legacy of broken dreams as the demands of 'blitzkrieg' battles continually outmoded the designs which were bequeathed, albeit with some alterations in the interim, from World War I.

The situation was indeed most serious. They knew that without a bridge that would meet the exacting new criteria of mobile warfare a skilful and professional enemy could keep our armies at bay in perpetuity. One has to advance to win battles and without a bridge to replace one destroyed there could be no advance. It was as simple as that.

Speed of erection, simplicity of design, flexibility, and strength were the keys to the concept which would be the solution. But no such design existed. There was not even an acceptable temporary substitute for the bridge anywhere else in the world. Even the Americans were using equipment at that time which was either more primitive or less suitable than the bridge they had seen buckle under its test load that morning. It was a desperate situation and their mood was grim. Something had to be produced somehow in this race against time. What was to be done? Where could one go next? What would the army commanders say? Worse still, what would Churchill himself have to say? It was more than just a miserable grey day. It was black, very black.

Little did Miss Dunn-Patterson, driving the Humber staff car, realize that her passengers would now unveil in her vehicle an idea which was to make a revolutionary impact on the conduct of the war and to provide a solution to what seemed then to be an insoluble problem. Captain S. A. (Stair) Stewart, in charge of the Experimental Bridging Establishment (EBE) at Christchurch in the south of England, felt it opportune to get Donald Bailey, his chief bridge designer, to explain to the third passenger what they had in mind. The third passenger was Colonel Fowle, Stewart's boss, based in London.

It was then that Donald Bailey, a man of such modesty and self-effacement that only aged veterans may possibly remember him, broke the silence. He spoke about the idea which had first come to him in 1936 and which, in the preceding months of 1940, he had suggested to his officer colleagues in the Royal Engineers, namely the supportive Captain Stair Stewart and Captain Alfred Jarrett-Kerr.

Perhaps the fact that Bailey was a Yorkshireman explains the doggedness with which he hung on in pursuit of his idea. He endured years of frustration caused by red tape complacency and the short-sightedness of people in high places—not an unusual experience for the few men of genius who have had to combat bureaucratic opposition. It was an invention so simple and yet so important that it provided the Allied armies with the possibility of victory.

It was an invention of such flexibility and multipurpose use that it became commonplace and almost taken for granted, and its real significance completely uncomprehended. It is still in use today all over the world, its basic concept virtually unchanged. As he leant forward in the car he used a device to explain his brainchild which deserves a paragraph of its own.

The British are among the most enthusiastic jotters on the backs of envelopes in the world. The widespread use of this medium is encouraged by its very availability in most pockets, and by the fact that its small

3

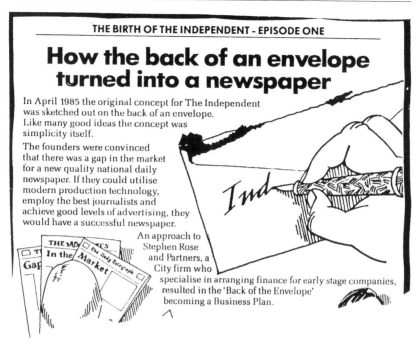

This advertisement which appeared in the mid-1980s shows how the *Independent* newspaper, like the Bailey Bridge, began its life on the back of an envelope. *Saatchi & Saatchi*

dimensions concentrate the mind wonderfully. There is no room for frills or fuss. Anyone who can condense and explain something on the back of an envelope gets quickly to the core of the matter. An advertisement from the mid 1980s proves the point. Those of us who are already devotees of the back-of-an-envelope system will not be at all surprised that one was used to plan the *Independent* newspaper!

So it was that Donald Bailey took out an envelope and drew on it, in a few deft lines, the shape of his idea. His colleagues immediately saw the point. They recognized that this could provide the solution to the problem and their salvation. But would it work in practice?

The very next day they got down to making preliminary calculations. Donald Bailey lost no time in showing his envelope to Alfred Jarrett-Kerr. Together they discussed the design features which would be required, and Alfred was entrusted with working out many important and complicated sums. The concept was not entirely new to him because Donald Bailey had raised it with him and Stair Stewart several times during the preceding months. Responding to the inspiration of the idea they stuck at their task without a break until figures emerged which gave sufficient

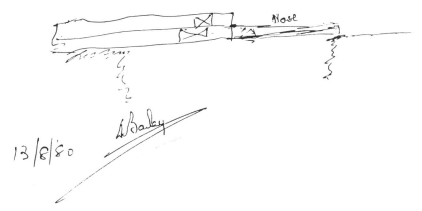

This version of the famous sketch by Donald Bailey, first drawn on the back of an envelope in 1940, was re-drawn and signed by him 40 years later at the author's request. *Harpur*

encouragement for them to contact the War Office. As a result, permission was given for the project to gain at last, after four weary wasted years, official status. This meant that resources would be provided to check it out properly. The sketch on Bailey's envelope was about to be translated into reality. He did not shout or burst into tears as he was entitled to do. He just took his pipe out of his mouth and breathed a long sigh of relief.

I met Donald Bailey in a humble bungalow near Bournemouth one summer day in 1980. He was then getting on a bit, having been born on 15 September 1901. He could only walk with difficulty. His speech was slow and slurred. This was the result of a series of strokes which he had suffered at intervals a few years earlier. But his mind was clear as will be demonstrated later in the narrative concerning his career.

His attentive wife bustled around serving up delicious tea and biscuits and prompting him now and again as he answered my many questions. With his permission I recorded the whole of our conversation on a cassette which I often re-play to capture again the magic of his amazing story.

One of the many questions I put to him concerned that legendary envelope and his alleged doodle on the back of it. I asked him if this were really true and he confirmed that it was. I then asked him if, 40 years later, he could still remember exactly what he drew on that historic envelope. He immediately got a piece of plain white paper and without hesitation, though with a trembling hand, reproduced his diagram exactly. He signed it at my request and gave it to me to keep. I treasure it with pride and a copy of it is reproduced here. I doubt if a layman can make head or tail of it. All those funny squiggles and crosses and

5

the insertion of the inexplicable word 'nose' combine to make it very puzzling. To the uninitiated it would be utterly incomprehensible. But he provided a commentary to go with it when he talked it through with his colleagues. Because of their background and training it made sense to them immediately. The explanation of it all will become very evident in the ensuing chapters.

Who exactly was this bald-headed, middle-aged man whose name nobody knew until halfway through the War, and who was a humble Civil Servant for most of his life? Donald Coleman Bailey was born in Rotherham, Yorkshire, on 18 September 1901, not far from his later home in Sheffield. He seemed to have had no outstanding memory of his days at his preparatory school in Derbyshire nor of his time at Rotherham Grammar School nor why at the age of 15 his father sent him to The Leys School, Cambridge, a year or more older than the average age of entry. Thanks to Mr John Stirland who was over 80 years of age when I corresponded with him and who was a master at Leys from 1919 to 1955, obviously the school's 'Mister Chips', I gleaned something about Donald Bailey's lack of impact. He wrote: 'He and I must have slept under the same roof of North House 'B' to which I went as a junior housemaster in January 1919 straight from World War I and Donald Bailey was there—had been in that House since 1916 and left in summer of 1919. The sad thing is that I have no recollection of him—no image, nothing. Some boys seem to have that effect, or non-effect. There is no record of his having played for any school teams. Bailey seems to be a typical example of the boy who passes through his school without leaving any mark or showing any special promise but who gains distinction in later life.'

In other words he might be described as doing in a sense a 'Winston Churchill' whose introduction to Harrow was effected, according to Sir Winston, solely by his being able to write his name and nothing else on his entrance examination paper. This was followed by a similarly undistinguished school career.

A few of Bailey's recollections of his days at Leys are interesting: 'I was there while the First World War was on and food was not very plentiful. The worst thing was having to get up early in the morning for a swim at 7 a.m. One had to learn to dive from a very high board, [which] could have been all of 20 feet (6 metres) above the water, and another test was to swim two lengths fully clothed! The only way to avoid some of the unpleasant things like these was to go to the sick room for a "chitty" as an excuse for absence which many of the boys did. I seemed to be one of the few who was always rumbled and it didn't work.'

When I asked him if at this stage he had shown any tendency to invent things he smiled: 'I had one or two what I thought would be interesting projects which not only turned out to be failures but had no future anyway. Still I was tempted to experiment with strange notions simply because for no apparent reason they came haphazardly to mind.

'My memory is uncertain now but I remember reading about one of my alleged schoolboy exploits which could well be true. I thought I could make a raft out of a metal frame instead of the usual wood on the assumption that if I could stretch sacking across it and make it watertight then it would not only float but, if the area covered was sufficiently large to equalize my displacement weight, it might support me as well. So I am told I bought a large iron bedstead for a few shillings from a scrap merchant or somebody. I found some canvas and painted it and stretched it over the frame. I must have had visions of sailing up and down the River Cam on it, but of course when launched it sank without trace. Perhaps more to the point in applying my elementary knowledge of engineering was an attempt I made to build, in a secluded part of the school, from a variety of strange parts, an engine powered by gas, I believe it worked in some sort of a way but of course such activity had to be stopped before I blew the school up.'

However, despite leaving Leys with no noticeable imprint of his time there, he did get a leaving certificate of sufficient grade to satisfy the requirements for admission to university. He talked this over with his father—the choice being between Sheffield and Cambridge. Eventually he decided on Sheffield which was not only where his home was but was better known for practical engineering studies.

'Cambridge was too theoretical' he said 'and besides after years of going to Leys I could not bear the tedious railway journey and above all having to change at Kettering'. His aversion to railway stations was confirmed by his friend Mr Denis Delany who worked with him. Mr Delany said 'Donald had a rooted objection to hanging about on railway stations and I remember, on more than one occasion, running a mile (and I mean running) all the way from Bush House in London to Waterloo Station in order to avoid having to wait 45 minutes for the next train. It was only pride that prevented me from suggesting to him that he should go on alone and I would follow at a more leisurely pace'.

Following this up I wrote to Sheffield University who were only too willing to provide information although, as at Leys School, this was somewhat sparse. However they confirmed that he was there from 1919 to 1923 and enclosed papers from his student record file. These are illuminating in respect of his academic prowess. It is apparent that during his first years he had very mixed fortunes. Some of the time he was ill, as a note from the Dean of the Faculty of Engineering to his father dated 16 March 1920 said. 'Dr Ripper is very sorry to hear that Donald Bailey has been so poorly and hopes that he will soon be better and able to return to his work.'

Then followed a mixed bag of 'passes' and 'fails' in his intermediate studies, and finally a crushing setback to his hopes when he sat for his final Bachelor of Engineering examination in 1922. He received a clinical five-word blow to his pride from the same Dr Ripper in a note (also sent to seven others) dated 28 June. It said starkly 'Failed to satisfy the Examiners'.

It says a lot for Bailey's character and resilience that the following year he walked out of Sheffield University, head high and eager to get going with the following tribute from the very same Dr Ripper folded neatly in his pocket dated 20 September 1923. 'I have the pleasure to state that Mr D. C. Bailey was a student in the Engineering Department of this University for the past four years taking the Degree Course in Civil Engineering. He was an attentive, capable, and painstaking student and did good work throughout. At the end of his course he succeeded in obtaining a Bachelor of Engineering Degree in the First Division. I have much pleasure in strongly recommending Mr Bailey to any firm or public body desiring services such as he is able to render.'

But his life at University and in the years that followed while he was still in his twenties was far more enterprising, he revealed, than just keeping his head down at a desk concentrating on his complicated academic studies. Not only did he play tennis for his University but he tried his hand at golf, which was later to become his main relaxation, and at cricket and hockey. He also earned some pocket money by mending watches. These repairs doubtless reflected his splendid capacity for doing things which needed mechanical precision. He also became keen on motorcycle racing at local events. 'My machine was an AJS 500cc and had a mind of its own' he remarked drily 'but although I never achieved very much on it I always liked pulling it to pieces and putting it together again. It was a lovely job, that machine, built in the days when, with the Norton, Brough, Triumph, Velocette, and others, we had the best bikes in the world.'

It seems that Donald Bailey would try his hand at anything which offered a physical challenge, because he progressed into some uneventful motor racing with an early Aston Martin and later, when he found himself posted to Wales on a railway assignment, he joined Abergavenny Rugby Club. 'I was a bit of a misfit' he said 'because I really wanted to be a forward and try my luck in the scrums, but I was like a bean pole and no matter what I did I could not put on enough weight.'

All this was happening during his final period at university and his subsequent first job in the Efficiency Department of Rowntrees, the cocoa factory in York. This was followed by an appointment which exercised his first real engineering experience in the Civil Engineering Department of the London Midland & Scottish Railway, the old 'LMS', as it used to be called.

He then transferred to Sheffield City Engineering Department where he made his mark during the construction of a new reservoir. Ever since his youthful days, as shown when he attempted his bedstead raft, he was fascinated by mastery of water in the shape of bridges and dams. The reservoir, built while he was still in his twenties, developed his expertise in civil engineering and his pride in construction, while providing a valuable public utility. It gave him enormous satisfaction. 'I found it the first really major challenge in a practical sense since I left University to test out all the theories and knowledge I had been taught. Water is a damnably difficult thing to tamper with. Even if it's only a pool on a roof, if there's a hole it will find it! Mind you, I did not do it alone. It was a great team effort and after all I was a comparative junior in the game. But I was really restless by then and desperate to move. I thought of going abroad but changed my mind when in 1928 I obtained the job of Civilian Engineer in what was then called the Experimental Bridging Establishment in Christchurch in the South of England.'

That such a pretentious title should hide such poverty of resources came as a shock to him. The Superintendent was a young man of modest rank in the Royal Engineers. There was only one draughtsman, although he had an occasional backup in the shape of a freelance who might come in on the odd occasion when the political situation in Europe took a particularly nasty turn, and it was felt that some concession should be made to the need to expand the drawing office.

The staff, virtually all civilian, consisted of only a score or so of assorted mechanics, metal workers, odd job men, and a 'bridging gang' of about five or six labourers who manhandled heavy equipment and bits of bridge around the adjoining open spaces. The wages were ludicrously low even for the time of the severe economic depression of the 1930s. It is a matter of record that when he started Donald Bailey was paid less than £400 p.a. Even allowing for the value of the pound sterling in those days this was a low salary for a man of his qualifications who had the awesome responsibility of being the sole designer of bridges. The money available for research and experimentation was virtually nil so that Bailey and his colleagues were forced to substitute brains and flair for the finance they needed. This was no bad thing perhaps because in 1936, at about the time when the concept of the Spitfire was taking shape, that wondrous aircraft which with the Hurricane won the great air Battle of Britain, Donald Bailey was thinking of the bridge that one day would help to win the war.

9

2 The Trauma of Termoli

IN any land battle the machine guns crackle, the artillery thunders, the tanks rumble, ground targets get swamped by aerial bombardment, barrages of shells explode, mortars unleash their high curving horror, and through the inferno, trembling and prayerful, moves the Soldier. His job is to capture and hold a bit of ground ahead of him. No matter how much support he gets by way of fire power, he ultimately is the key figure. The navy can put him on land, or take him off. The navy can bring their big guns to bear on the enemy holding him up. The navy can help to get the supplies he needs transported over the oceans. But the navy does not have to capture and hold the ground over which he has advanced. The Soldier does that. The air force can strafe and bomb his enemy's strongholds, drop supplies for him and even drop him by parachute behind the enemy lines. The air force can supply him with precise photographs of hostile terrain and help to observe enemy supplies and troop movements. But the air force does not have to capture and hold the ground over which he has advanced. The Soldier does that.

The army provides the Soldier with the raw materials of survival. The army trains him to be a killing machine. The army clothes him, feeds him, gives him medical and dental attention, arranges for his baths, laundry, recreation, and payment and above all gives him a short handle shovel so that he can dig or die. Finally, in that latter event, they arrange his burial and for his next of kin to be informed.

Throughout the history of conquest it is the realization that, when ground is lost to the enemy which cannot be recaptured, this brings defeat. But when the territory taken reaches such proportions that the victim no longer has the will nor the means to continue then he has to surrender totally.

At the end of every skirmish, every battle, every campaign, every war, there is the Soldier in victory in possession of the ground over which his weary feet have taken him. His presence and the absence of his foes provides the elementary proof of final triumph.

But the chain of administration which enables the Soldier to have what he needs to hold his ground is only as strong as his weakest link. Almost invariably that weakest link, when battle is joined, is within a few hundred yards of the Soldier in the shape of a river, chasm, ravine, or ditch which he has just crossed. That natural hazard, mined beforehand and shelled continuously by the enemy, stands between the Soldier and his tank support, his reinforcements, his extra ammunition, his anti-tank guns, his food, his medical supplies, his dry socks, and last but not by any means least, letters from home.

Now it is an axiom of war, universally accepted, that when the Soldier advances and then pauses to consolidate his gains, he must be counter-attacked as soon as possible before that consolidation enables him to hold his position. So speed in getting support and supplies to him is a vital consideration. If the service is slow, the retreat is fast.

The defenders have always counted upon the natural barriers of rivers and ravines to halt the advance of the adversary, especially in modern warfare when bridges everywhere were blown to smithereens, thus denying a crossing point for troops and tanks.

The painful process of the Eighth and Fifth Armies in Italy where there was always 'one more river to cross' testified to the delay, frustration, and casualties inflicted on them by the enemy. In fact all but one of the many great defensive lines built in such formidable depth by the Germans were based on Italy's daunting and torrential rivers.

That apt cliché 'the poor bloody infantry' was never so relevant as when the first to make a river crossing had to swim or wade or haul themselves by a slender rope. If they were lucky they might risk a shaky navigation in a wooden, canvas or inflatable assault boat which one stray bullet could sink. Wet, confused, miserable, and fearful, they would advance, those that were left of them, through minefields and wire entanglements, silhouetted by enemy flares and harassed by rockets, mortar bombs, and shells.

River crossings were made by night to minimize casualties but that compounded the difficulty both of keeping contact with each other and of essential ammunition ferried in small quantities along a pitifully inade-quate supply line reaching them. Then the dreaded dawn would come and with it the enemy tanks to overrun our Soldier unless by some miracle he got his tank or anti-tank gun first.

So if one accepts the simple precept that ground gained must be held if a war is to be won, one will appreciate that against a courageous, battle-trained enemy, speedy and skilled in combat, one had to have something very special to ensure that the Soldier got what he needed in

11

time to hold his ground and then to advance again. This was inevitably a bridge, a very special kind of bridge, which could be erected in time to allow the passage of tanks and supplies to reach the Soldier before the weight of the enemy's counter-attack threw him back.

Donald Bailey's brilliant idea produced such a bridge which became the key to victory. It was a bridge the like of which had never been seen anywhere before in its simplicity and speed of erection. No other nation could match it. The Germans were denied it because once it was introduced they never had the opportunity of capturing one because it always ensured their constant retreat. The Russians envied it. The Americans adopted it. The engineers of many different armies from different countries on the Allied side were given access to it and they loved it. The Canadians, for example, romped through Europe with it in a series of what they called the 'bridge gallop' in which they leap-frogged each other in building bridges in quick succession.

To illustrate the vital role the bridge played in the winning of land battles, I can draw upon a personal experience. The very thought of it still makes me tense. Always I am reminded of Wellington's terse appraisal of his victory at Waterloo as being a 'damned close-run thing'. I was a witness of a World War II battle which was possibly more of a 'damned close-run thing' than that which shook the Iron Duke. It was a battle of immense significance even though it did not rank by name in the same category as Cassino or El Alamein. For those involved it was a nightmare. Indeed it was worse than a nightmare because there was no waking up to the relief of finding it was just a bad dream. On the contrary there was very little or no sleep at all to awake from. It was so much touch and go, so much in the balance, a balance so delicate, so finely poised, that the scales could well have trembled at the last faint gasp of a dying man; and there were many who died.

What was conceived as little more than an interesting skirmish turned into a trauma when only a few minutes separated what might have been the first major defeat of Britain's vaunted Eighth Army since El Alamein, and a propaganda victory for Hitler. After more than 40 years the memory of the havoc and horror, and the heroism, of this epic confrontation between 10,000 of the fighting elite of the British and German forces has not been erased.

It was in the first few fateful days of October 1943 that it happened. It was a time when the eyes of the western world were looking to the Italian campaign as the major theatre of war. It was three months before the Cassino battles, nine months before D-Day, and many months before the German forces started to wilt before the Russian onslaught and the Americans jolted the Japanese.

The setting was an idyllic seaside resort called Termoli, nestling at the foot of undulating hills and distant mountains. It was a tiny piece of paradise with a picturesque harbour nudging its elbow gently against the temperamental Adriatic. Its buildings grouped becomingly on different levels were dominated by the campanile. The ancient church presided in quiet dignity over the village square where footpaths were etched by the faithful on the stones leading to its sanctuary. It was an inviting prospect which, once seen, called for the immediate despatch of a picture postcard with the message 'Wish you were here'. Its tranquillity was shattered, however, when it became the focal point for a complicated and hazardous military operation.

Towards the end of September 1943 the final plans were made by the Eighth Army advancing along the east coast of Italy to capture Termoli. It was no more than a small name on the map but it was noted that it had a useful little harbour and that the railway line hugging the flat ground near the shores of the Adriatic passed through it. These features could provide a vital link in the chain of administration for bringing up rations, petrol, and ammunition to maintain the momentum of the advance. The planners encircled the name 'Termoli' with chinagraph pencils on the talc of their map cases with relish. Here was a little gem of an objective. Its capture would provide answers simultaneously to many supply problems and cause alarm and despondency among the retreating enemy.

It was a daring plan, and one that was designed primarily to avoid the casualties and delays caused by the Germans blowing their bridges as they withdrew. It was anticipated correctly that the main structure crossing the steep-banked and wide River Biferno, the one nearest to Termoli, would be destroyed.

The first move was to send in a Commando unit to make a surprise night attack from the sea on the town itself. This would by-pass the mouth of the River Biferno and completely neutralize the effect of its bridges being destroyed. This move would also cut off the retreat of some of the enemy and disrupt his communications.

The Commandos would then hang on to the town, forming a small perimeter around it, and await the arrival of the British infantry and tanks having by this time forced the crossing of the Biferno. A simple, daring plan which in terms of ringcraft might be described as leading with a stylish right hook to the enemy's left earhole followed up by a full-blooded upper cut with the left fist on his chin. But in the event there was a nasty surprise. The enemy's chin was not as weak as had been thought and then they socked us with a damn great blow on our left earhole. In boxing terms they had us on the ropes. There was no time-keeper to sound the respite. This match was a one-round fight to the finish — but of course at the time we did not know it.

Luckily, as it turned out, the Eighth Army had as its spearhead the famous British 78th Division, veterans of great battles in Tunisia, Sicily and in the invasion of Italy. It was truly British, comprising regiments from Lancashire, Northampton, Kent, Surrey, London, mixing with Scotland's Argyll and Sutherland Highlanders, the Irish Brigade's Inniskillings, London Irish, and Royal Irish Fusiliers, all supported by Welsh Gunners and the sappers — British to the core. It was their task to storm the Biferno and link up with the Commandos.

To explain my unique vantage point for observing the operations, I was sent to occupy high ground a mile or so up-river from the Biferno crossing to protect our left flank. I was then commanding a machine-gun company. The water-cooled Vickers Medium Machine Gun weighed, with tripod, nearly 100 pounds (45 kilograms). It was held in great respect and affection by us because simply by finger touch and well drilled reflex one had to diagnose and rectify within seconds up to a dozen identifiable stoppages. There are not many weapons as interesting as that!

So it was that by 1 October 1943 I was able to see clearly, even without binoculars, the whole of the panorama of mountains and hills running gradually down towards Termoli on the enemy side of the river. We were well dug in. Our guns were taking in a broad arc of fire across the valleys from which enemy patrols crossing over the river might emerge to attack or probe our left flank. Sentries were changed throughout every 24 hours, two hours on, four hours off. I liaised with our infantry beside us. It rained like hell. We got wet. We got very hungry. Rations were running out. Cigarettes had nearly all gone. A fag was passed around for one puff per person until the final recipient burned his lips. Huddled around in our ground sheets which doubled as rain capes, we waited, waited, waited. This was the war nobody raves about and yet this was what most of active service (did I say 'active'?) in the front line was all about.

Suddenly we heard the unmistakable sound of a vehicle crashing its way uphill through the mud. We could hear it slewing about on spinning wheels as its engine roared. Transfixed by the mystery of it all because normally the only wheeled vehicle this far forward would be a motorcycle, we were amazed to see a three-ton lorry, one of ours, edge towards us. As it got closer I could just make out the occupant beside the driver, devouring a king-size bully-beef sandwich. Our mouths watered. It was all I could do to stop a mutiny when at last the lorry halted and my second-in-command stepped down from the cab, his mouth bulging with that massive delicacy. 'I've brought your rations' he announced. His mouth was so full we thought he had finished them. There was a roar of laughter. By God, we were pleased to see him. The indomitable Captain Teddy Cullen, whose long pointed nose and receding chin belied both his great boxing skill and grim determination, was our pride and joy. No matter where I and my men were, he was sure to find us. Little things like finding himself in a room with a grenade he had thrown and which bounced back off a window and exploded seemed to leave him unscathed. That night, the night the terror of Termoli began which was yet to reach us, we had full stomachs, two packets of cigarettes per man, some letters from home, an issue of rum, and—absolute bliss—a change of socks.

While we were counting our blessings in the eerie darkness and watching the intermittent flashes of gunfire light up the clouds with sudden silver, the Commandos were on their way. Their landing craft by some miraculous navigation, and with noise of their approach masked by shellfire, found Termoli. The surprise was complete and soon the town was in their hands.

Within 24 hours their ranks had been swollen by the arrival by sea of 36th Infantry Brigade and some others of the 78th Division. The blown bridge did not stop the Lancashire Fusiliers wading over the river. Eight anti-tank guns were sent over by raft and by dusk a folding boat bridge was in use. Things looked good. They confirmed the saying that sometimes things are too good to be true.

The disturbing fact was that there was no bridge as yet which was strong enough to permit our tanks to join our forces. So the small garrison of Termoli was cut off from vital supporting armour before its bridgehead could be expanded to ensure its security. Then it began to pour with rain again, creating quagmires in which vehicles got bogged down. In addition enemy air activity increased and their fighter-bombers concentrated on the crossing over the Biferno.

Suddenly everyone became aware of an awesome possibility: What if the Germans launched a counter-attack on Termoli before the reinforcements could get through? With their heavy tank support, operating in country which they knew well, the Germans could drive downhill on Termoli. The British garrison would be crushed and literally driven into the sea. The Eighth Army would suffer a grievous defeat and their advance halted ignominiously. The early hope of success which admitted no such fear was now being replaced by the terror which this very real danger inspired. Murphy's law states that if anything can go wrong, it will. It was as if the anticipation of impending disaster had attracted it. The importance of Termoli was not lost on the Germans, who even before the Commandos entered the town had switched unexpectedly from their Naples front, on the far side of Italy, the tanks and infantry of their crack 16th Panzer Division. They arrived in good order, having traversed a route of several hundreds of miles across the Appenines.

One of the first to learn of their presence was a brother officer in my regiment who, with his machine gun company, had been among the few to cross the Biferno. Captain Bertie Page, a small, quiet, self-effacing, pipe-smoking, young man, had the heart of a lion. He was sent with his men up to a group of houses called San Giacoma, which stood in a wooded area in the hills a mile or so above Termoli. It was supposed to be manned by our own troops but he was shocked to discover that the Germans had got there first. He withdrew without being seen and immediately deployed his guns to cover the line of the German advance.

15

But before they could even dig in properly, enemy tanks rumbled forward. It was no contest against such armour. Captain Page's guns were shot up with high explosive and overrun. Serious casualties resulted. He himself killed or wounded three of the enemy who had left their tank, at point blank range, and made a daring escape, bringing with him the vital news of the enemy thrust. He was awarded an immediate Military Cross for this gallant work.

At the same time from my magnificent observation post in perfect safety I was watching the build-up of the German attack all along the far ridges leading down to Termoli. It seemed as if the whole of the Panzer Division was deployed moving from left to right in front of my eyes in a re-enactment of a Cecil B. De Mille film epic with a cast of thousands. I watched with amazement groups of their grey-coated soldiers crouching behind their tanks as they edged slowly forward. They put down smoke to try and keep their vulnerable flank from being exposed to our artillery on the south side of the river. This was only partially successful because eddies of wind blowing off the sea frequently lifted the cover. Through a curtain rising intermittently, we caught glimpses of the enemy forming and re-forming as they found their way over wooded spurs and out into the open again. By now, warned by wireless link with our observers, the Termoli garrison was on full alert. They knew, and we knew, everybody knew, that unless they got tank support the Panzer Division would simply roll over them and all would be lost.

Suddenly an obstinate inanimate object became the agonizing centre of attention. All now depended on it. It was the new bridge which the sappers were trying to push across the Biferno. If this was not completed in time to let our armour through to Termoli, all would be lost. The Germans knew this too as their strafing from the air was supplemented by increasingly accurate shellfire.

Yard by yard I watched the Panzer tanks advance. Somewhat frustrated because I had been ordered to keep my guns facing our own left flank for fear of the enemy appearing on our side of the river, instead of engaging the visible enemy in a classic enfilade field of fire, I did something quite unforgivable. I crawled forward to the tiny camouflaged hideout of an artillery forward-observation officer about 50 yards (45 metres) in front of me on a forward slope. The FOO lives a scary existence because if he is to direct the ranging of his guns, usually sited far behind, he has to see where the shells fall. This means that the enemy can see him, that is if they can find him. So by moving towards him I could be exposing his position. What I was trying to find out was the precise range for engaging the enemy in case I was allowed to bring my guns into action, and also if he had any news to illuminate the fog of war. He was there all by himself in a tiny hollow operating his wireless set with great composure under his small camouflage net. He withheld his irritation long enough to give me an average range and then told me to bugger off before we were shelled. But he said it nicely. Gunners too are a special breed. I sensed also his frustration at getting such weak support from his battery because of shortage of shells, when such tempting targets offered themselves.

As the morning wore on I could tell by the crackle of small arms fire and the bursts of exploding shells how much nearer the enemy tanks were getting towards Termoli itself. Despite fierce resistance by the crack Commandos and the veterans of the 78th neither topography nor time were on our side. It became increasingly obvious that the whole outcome of this ferocious battle depended on how quickly that vital bridge could be built if we were to relieve Termoli before the Panzer tanks swept in. It was estimated that if the situation were to be saved, that precious bridge had to be ready to carry our tanks by no later than 3 p.m. that afternoon. By midday the Germans were now only a few miles from Termoli, with about three hours in hand against the bridge deadline.

We had to delay them. Every minute counted. Our artillery intensified. Air support was hampered by low clouds, rain, and bad visibility. On the credit side this affected adversely the enemy fighter attacks on the Biferno crossing. The garrison gave ground but only inch by inch. The sweating sappers worked away at what was in effect our only hope—that bloody bridge. Would it be finished in time? In this nail-biting situation 'time' was the only four-letter word which took temporary priority over that other four-letter word normally used by the poor bloody infantry as a healthy expletive, especially in crises. 'Ask me for anything except time' Napoleon told his Generals. Never was time so much needed. Days had been reduced to hours. Hours were now coming down to minutes. What the hell was happening about that bridge? We felt even the seconds tick by as if generated by some maddening metronome. We did not know what it was like down there at the crossing. Only the sappers could know that.

What we were not aware of at that time were the vital but false assumptions on which the battle plan had been based. First of all the deluge of rain, 18 hours of continuous downpour, was completely unexpected. The 78th Division planners were misled by inaccurate weather information, the official forecast being for a reasonably dry period until the end of the month. It was certainly not scheduled to break four weeks earlier, as in the event it did.

Secondly, Eighth Army's Intelligence was confident that, apart from the German parachute division retreating before us, Termoli was held by only a small garrison unlikely to be reinforced before we had made it thoroughly secure. The unexpected arrival of the 16th Panzer Division put paid to that happy prospect.

Thirdly, although by wading and using small boats the infantry, together with a few anti-tank guns, had crossed the Biferno before the rains turned it into a raging torrent, the sappers were then forced to contrive a small bridge without having the proper bridging equipment. It seems monstrous in retrospect, but this had been 'borrowed' by Eighth Army from the Division for railway repairs. The bridge they had substituted was incapable of taking the heavy load of tanks or even the gunners' anti-tank guns.

The Division's Irish Brigade was now on its way by sea blissfully unaware of what to expect when they got to Termoli. The Commander observed 'as far as my Brigade was concerned it was to be a pleasant peacetime cruise, with fighting unlikely for a fortnight or so. Termoli was known to be a nice little town.' He then added ruefully 'Note: This did not go according to plan.' They arrived at a critical time, quite surprised that the war was still on. Seven landing craft put them into the battered harbour and they disembarked at the rate of 300 men every 90 minutes. They were all fresh and braced for battle after a serene and uneventful voyage.

It was a day of drizzle and of destiny. The Argylls were in exposed positions holding off the German tanks and infantry with precious few anti-tank guns and no tank support at all. The guns of the Division's 17th Field Regiment were putting down a curtain of fire with limited ammunition just 100 yards (90 metres) ahead of them in a bid to stem the grey tide of the Panzer Division's advance.

The sappers under shellfire managed to make a ford over which six tanks of the City of London Yeomanry trundled on to the Termoli side before the river became impassable again. These tanks went to the support of the gallant Argylls with great dash but four were knocked out. The remainder and the infantry had to fall back to the shelter of a brickworks, a couple of miles outside the town. These brickworks were now being heavily shelled by *both* sides and Major Anderson, the hero of the Longstop Hill attack in North Africa where he had won his VC, was killed. He was one of the 12 officers killed or wounded and 150 casualties among the other ranks of the Argylls who were still retiring in good order through the positions occupied by the Lancashire Fusiliers.

Gunner officers who had gone forward with the leading troops as forward observation officers found themselves fighting for their lives as infantrymen. Even the dressing stations of the Division's Royal Army Medical Corps were cut off at times and suffered many casualties when hit by shellfire.

While the Argylls were withdrawing, the men of the Royal West Kents and the Buffs were also falling back under the pressure of the enemy tanks. The few anti-tank guns at our disposal could not be moved forward to assist, simply because they were now completely bogged down in tenacious mud. The awesome Mark IV tanks of the Panzer Division overran the Royal West Kents and then turned towards the Buffs. The withdrawal was stemmed temporarily as the Royal West Kents, now down to just 80 men, took up new positions.

That afternoon of 5 October, it seemed all would be lost unless a miracle happened. There were 30 tanks waiting just the other side of the river and what was needed was a heavy tank-bearing bridge to enable them to join the battle in time to save the day. Again the agonizing questions were in the minds of our hard-pressed soldiers. What the hell was happening about that bridge? If there was a bridge, would it be finished in time?

By some miracle, as it turned out, it was. The Army had returned the proper bridging equipment which would enable the answers to these questions to be found. The sappers went into action. They knew it was a matter of life and death. Their estimate of the time needed to finish the job was, given good luck, 24 hours. This set the 3 p.m. deadline as being the most optimistic one could expect.

The 214th Field Company of the Royal Engineers charged with the responsibility of building the bridge had first to clear away a vast amount of rubble from a damaged arch and also to make good part of the road over another damaged arch, both left standing after the bridge was blown. This took a long time to finish but the major setback was the fact that the bridge was always in range of the enemy artillery. It was going to be a very long job, not only because it had to be a very long bridge, but because work had to be constantly interrupted to avoid the shellfire and to deal with the casualties.

One shell landed on the road just above the bridge on the home side and wounded no less than eight men. Not just any old eight men, but men who were trained and skilled for essential jobs on the bridge. But work went on and replacements from another platoon arrived. There was virtually a round-the-clock rota system to build up the brick wall supporting one of the arches and at the same time to deliver, off-load, and assemble the multitude of bridge components. Everything militated against speed. The casualties had reduced the Company to half strength for the building. The vehicles bringing up the equipment were trapped in the entrance to their assembly area by the glutinous mountains of mud due to the incessant rain. As fast as the vehicles arrived they were hastily unloaded. No man had any rest. The shells still kept coming but, encouraged by the fact that many fell short, work went on. But not all fell short and one vicious burst, again on the road nearby, felled three sappers instantly, one of whom was mortally wounded.

Sweating, heaving, cursing, the sappers were now running at the double to and fro with their heavy loads: it took six men to carry just one item. Shocked by shellfire, utterly fatigued but doggedly racing backwards and forwards to their appointed tasks, minute by minute they caught up on their 3 p.m. deadline. Could they do it? The rest of us waited.

Meanwhile the Panzer tanks were moving forward and it was only a matter of minutes now, not hours, before the final outcome would be achieved one way or the other. The world still waited—the world of the soldier, that is, whose future had shrunk to the size of a hastily dug slit trench as he prepared to die. It was a simple matter of waiting. . . . waiting . . . waiting. Fate moves very slowly at such times.

Despite the rain, the appalling conditions, and the constant shellfire, the sappers worked on. They must have had the burning faith that moves mountains not only in their skills but also in the quality and design of their bridging equipment which they knew from previous experience would not let them down. It would do the job, if they did theirs.

Thanks to Cyril Ray's excellent history of the 78th Division entitled *Algiers to Austria*, one is able to record that the bridge 'was finished at 2.40 p.m. in the afternoon of 5 October'. This was 20 minutes earlier than the deadline. Twenty vital minutes when our Sherman tanks raced over. They attacked the enemy tanks on a plateau overlooking our positions. By dusk the battle was stabilized but our bridgehead was still ringed by the tanks and infantry of the crack 16th Panzer Division, and the enemy shellfire was not letting up. Five of the first nine Shermans were knocked out, and there were at least 25 Panzer Mark IV tanks still in action. It is now recognized that those few Shermans had prevented the enemy from moving in for the final kill which, understandably, they fully expected to do.

At dusk that same night the turning point of this bitter battle arrived in the shape of two squadrons of the Canadian Tank Regiment crossing over that sturdy bridge. They joined up with the fresh Irish Brigade and also with the tanks of the City of London Yeomanry and attacked early next morning. Again the fighting was fierce, but bit by bit the enemy was forced back. By nightfall the trauma of Termoli was over. The Germans were retreating in considerable disorder.

The next morning I and my Company crossed that bridge without realizing we were treading on glorious history. We arrived in Termoli to strengthen the defences in case the Germans came back, as they often did. Shells were still flying around. Things were not pleasant. But I recall vividly a series of postscripts which sealed for ever this time capsule buried in my mind.

A much beloved brother officer of mine in another part of my battalion, which rejoiced in the name of Princess Louise's Kensington Regiment, was called Henry Page (no relation to Bertie Page mentioned previously). With bright blue eyes, a smiling boyish face, a gift for scoring tries on the wing playing rugby, for always taking bets, and for finding useful items that fell off the back of the proverbial lorry, he was a fine warrior. He came rushing into Termoli with the ecstatic announcement 'There's an abandoned German tank near the brickworks. Betcha we could take it over.' Then he added as a precautionary afterthought, although not to be taken too seriously 'It's only got a little hole in it.' With that he extended his right arm and pressing his index finger against his thumb to form a fleshy circle he waved it in front of us to emphasize its size. It was then I realized once again how close the Germans had got to success. The brickworks were only about a mile or so from both the town and the sea and this was where their tank was stopped.

Twenty minutes later poor Henry Page was taken out of Termoli on a stretcher with one eye and half his face blown away. Accurate enemy shelling of the town was causing considerable disruption and Henry had been hit by a sizeable splinter. Amazingly he survived and lived long enough to enliven our post-war reunions for several years before he died. We missed him greatly.

The reason for the severe shelling of Termoli throughout the battle was eventually traced to the campanile where a resourceful German officer was hiding with a wireless set. From his privileged observation post in the middle of the town he could call for fire wherever and whenever congestion of troops and vehicles took place. This coincidence eventually led to the deduction that somebody in the town must be responsible for alerting the enemy artillery and, almost as a last resort, the campanile was searched.

My last memory of Termoli before we moved on after licking our wounds, was the sight of the indomitable Teddy Cullen dashing along the skyline seemingly in full view of the enemy. He was flinging notes about like confetti as he insisted on paying out to our Company in their most forward positions. It seems mad now, but yes, we did get regular pay 'in the field' with some sort of Mickey Mouse money deputizing for genuine lire. Teddy was not one to overlook the chance of getting into the action. On this occasion the enemy must have been otherwise occupied, or just as bemused as we were, in watching the antics of what appeared to be a demented figure.

PONDERING ON all these things from time to time I was eventually stunned by something I had never appreciated. I did not learn until nearly 40 years later the amazing story of the bridge. I am not talking of the men who built it, although their achievement is amazing enough, but of the bridge itself. Because as I have already explained, it was a special kind of structure. Its like had never been seen in action before 1943 and nor was it ever bettered since. It was the only creation anywhere in the world which was capable of being built at the speed which the deadline demanded. No matter how resourceful were our engineers, no matter their numbers, no matter the conditions, only this bridge, rightly described as the 'marvel of the war', enabled the job to be done. It was designed, as I have just said, among other things for speed of erection.

In the terror of Termoli men bought time with their lives. It was the bridge, and the bridge alone, which made victory possible in the nick of that time which had been bought so dearly.

21

3 The Umbilical Bridge

B Y now the reader will have appreciated that if one is going to bring tanks and supplies in sufficient quantity on the same side of a river as the beleaguered infantry, one needs a bridge. Also one has to have a flexible bridge, capable not only of taking the weight of tanks of great tonnage but also of being constructed and put across various widths of river in a matter of a few hours by a handful of men. Up until 1941 there was no bridge anywhere in the world which could meet these criteria. The millions of bridges used year in and year out for civilian traffic were custom-built jobs to meet the varying needs of length, width, and loading for each crossing and could take years to build. Some picturesque bridges erected centuries ago still remain to remind us that nothing is so taken for granted as a bridge until one day it is no longer there.

Yet there is nothing boring about a bridge. In fact if you scratch an engineer you don't draw blood. He draws a bridge. To appreciate the skills of engineers it is necessary to make a few obvious points about bridge building. Let us take an ordinary plank, say 20 feet (6 metres) long, a foot (30 centimetres) wide, and two inches (5 centimetres) deep. If you put it over a stream say 15 feet (4.5 metres) wide the ends will overlap the ground on either side by a division of the remaining five feet.

The vital consideration is weight. Depending on this a number of things might happen when you walk along the plank. If you are heavy enough it will crack or shear right off at the edge of the stream where there is no longer any ground to support the plank. If your weight is less you may survive that, but the plank will start to sag ominously as you get towards the middle and probably break. But if the plank rests upon strong supports provided by girders on either side of it then its ability to avoid sagging or breaking is obviously improved. So it follows that the path or roadway over a river must be supported from underneath or along its sides, or by both, to withstand the weight of the maximum load envisaged.

My preoccupation with this over-simplified crash course into some of the mysteries of bridging is solely to raise a number of essential points. The most obvious one is that a bridge is about as useful as a glass eye to a sniper if it does not reach the other side. Another important observation is that if the sides of a bridge are not strong enough to take the required weight imposed upon the decking or roadway they support, then they will bend, buckle, or break. Finally there is a limit to the length you can push out any bridge before it needs something to support it.

As I have said earlier, bridges, like many other familiar objects which are closely woven into the pattern of our everyday lives, are apt to be overlooked or taken for granted by the ordinary person. He or she is not concerned with the problems of design which have had to be solved before the bridge can withstand all the traffic loads and all the buffeting which may come on it, nor with the problems of erection inherent in getting some of these immense structures into place and providing foundations to keep them stable for generations.

One usually asks only that the bridge shall be there when required for the service and convenience it provides. Hardly a thought is spared for the research and toil which must go into its creation. But in time of war, flood, or earthquake, when a bridge is destroyed, the resultant chaos in communications focuses attention on its vital importance and one becomes very aware of its high priority in one's life. The late Franklin D. Roosevelt once said 'The story of bridge building is the story of civilization and by it we can readily measure an important part of a people's progress.'

To assess the quantum leap which Donald Bailey's concept represented, indeed to savour fully its revolutionary impact, it is helpful for the layman to be given a simple brief run-down on its evolution.

The people of the late Paleolithic or Stone Age had only the crudest tools of flint and bone. They were nomads, and as they moved about they needed structures to help them to cross ravines, chasms, and rivers. Man's eternal quest to find the shortest distance between two points was as paramount then as it is today. We can imagine that they would roam along a bank looking for a narrow and easy crossing. They would then with luck find a log which had fallen across the river connecting bank to bank—the first bridge. In other places they may have found natural arches, eroded by the water, in others they may have made use of the trailing tendrils of the liana vine—the first suspension bridge. Late Paleolithic man may have imitated nature by pulling a fallen tree across the stream where he could not find one already in place, but he could proceed no farther, because he lacked adequate tools.

About 15,000 BC Neolithic, or New Stone Age, culture evolved and man was the proud possessor of polished stone instruments, including the axe. Now it was possible to fashion simple structures, amongst them bridges. A tree could be felled and its branches lopped, making a bridge where none was before. Gradually various elaborations were introduced. The coming of the Bronze Age in about 5,000 BC brought with it the possibility of metal fastenings, opening the way to still greater developments.

And so through the centuries bridges evolved into what we know today, from the simple natural forms already described, to wooden pile bridges, stone arches, metal bridges, reinforced concrete bridges, pontoon bridges. (While the latter are still used to meet special circumstances from time to time it is a humbling thought to be reminded that the King of the Persians built a pontoon bridge on stuffed skins across the Euphrates in 537 BC!) Lake dwellers in Switzerland lived thousands of years ago in small timber houses built on pile-supported platforms over the water. From this to the post-and-girder timber-piled bridge was a logical step.

Many thrilling tales of the bridge in peace and war unfold as the pages of history turn. The eternal vision of posterity which inspires bridge builders is represented by the Roman Caius Julius Lacer who, having been commanded by the Emperor Trajan to bridge the River Tagus, exclaimed with pride on its completion 'I have left a bridge that shall remain for eternity.' His Alcantara Bridge linking the environs of Lisbon in fact lasted 2,000 years before being replaced in the mid 1960s.

River crossings with primitive bridges became the focal point for the growth of villages, then towns, and then cities. London is a prime example. The old London Bridge is part of world history but a Roman writer records one being there in AD 43. Many bridges were built on or near the same site. The first record of a Saxon bridge occurs in a 10th century account of some unfortunate women sentenced to death for witchcraft being drowned there. In 1163 Peter of Colechurch, priest and chaplain, built a timber bridge near the same spot. It was this same Peter who 13 years later began the building of the famous Old London Bridge which was to remain so closely linked with the life of London until 1831 when it was dismantled. Peter of Colechurch died in 1205 before the bridge was finished and was buried in a chapel on the bridge itself. The bridge was finally completed in 1209, having taken 33 years to build. It had 19 pointed arches with an impressive span of 936 feet (285 metres). Houses were gradually built on the bridge. In fact in Elizabeth I's time so fashionable an address was London Bridge that a group of young noblemen imported from Holland what may have been the first prefabricated house. This was a strange four-sided wooden structure, fastened together by wooden pegs. It came in pieces and was erected on the spot and was called Nonsuch House.

In AD 122 the Roman emperor Hadrian built a bridge around which

Newcastle developed into a great city in the North of England. Defoe wrote of it 'Some say indeed it exceeds all the bridges in England for strength, it is indeed very firm and wide having a street of houses upon it and a gate in the middle as large as a little castle.'

The earlier mention of Peter of Colechurch emphasizes the important role of the Church in building bridges, both in Britain and in Europe, where French and Italian religious orders trained and designated certain of their fraternity for this role. This was an extension of what today we would call 'industrial logic'. We see the patient priest building to the glory of God and for the good of his fellow men, probably guided in the proportions he chooses for his bridges by those proven so satisfactory for the arches in the naves of the great cathedral churches.

A notable milestone towards scientific design was the foundation in France in 1716 of the Corps des Ponts et Chaussées. From that time bridge design gradually developed from a matter of trial and error towards the remarkable precision which can be attained today. The Corps was charged with the task of approving the design of all bridges, canals, and roads and to ensure competence its members had to be graduates of the Ecole de Paris. It was a forerunner of the British Institution of Civil Engineers of which Thomas Telford became the first president in 1820 and which has ever since maintained a high standard for the professional engineers in many countries.

The coming of railways in the 19th century naturally caused an enormous increase in the requirements for bridges in Europe and America. In Britain, for example, no fewer than 16,000 were built in 70 years. It was a period of great triumphs and also of great disasters. It is as well to dwell briefly on the catastrophes from which such important lessons were learned.

During a terrible storm on a night in December 1889 the Edinburgh mail train was crossing the Tay Bridge in Scotland when watchers saw 'a flash of sparks in the darkness and then a long comet of light sweeping down to the waters of the Tay'. The train and much of the bridge disappeared for ever. It was the climax of a number of failures caused by wind pressure. An intensive study was immediately made of the forces which can be exerted by wind. After that it was thought that enough was known of wind effects to avoid all danger but a new form of failure occurred when the great 2,800 foot (853 metre) span of the Tacoma Narrows Suspension Bridge in the United States failed in 1940. This time comparatively light wind produced spectacular oscillations and twisting, causing the span to collapse only a few months after its completion. Subsequent investigation showed that this was due to aerodynamic instability of the flexible bridge deck (the 'road' surface) which is very similar to the phenomenon of wing flutter in aircraft. So, like the aeroplane designer, the bridge engineer has to make use of the wind tunnel to check the security of a structure of this kind.

25

There are other important considerations which the engineer has to take into account. The passage of traffic can set up a rhythm of vibration which can cause severe strain as it gathers momentum. For this reason there is a notice on London's Albert Bridge to this day which warns that troops on the march must break step when crossing it. Most mysterious of all are the strains due to changes of temperature. The material of the bridge contracts with the cold and expands with the heat with such irresistible force that the bridge builder must allow sufficient tolerance in his calculations to counter such variation. Strange as it may seem, one half hour of bright sunshine may be a more severe test of a bridge than the passage of a 350-ton train.

American engineers have had to meet the challenge of bridging enormous rivers and of linking islands and estuaries. Their expertise with magnificent suspension bridges is well demonstrated by the San Francisco 'Golden Gate' Bridge.

But what is perhaps not so well known is that when originally built three of the largest suspension bridges in the world spanned East River at New York City. In the famous Brooklyn bridge two huge towers of masonry held aloft four steel cables from which the roadway was supported. To make the cables, more than 5,000 steel wires were woven into a rope as thick as a man's body. Downward over the water they curved from the towers and back to land on the other side, where their ends were anchored securely in blocks of masonry buried deep in the earth. The other two suspension bridges, the Manhattan and Williamsburg bridges, had steel towers instead of masonry. The Williamsburg bridge had a river span of 1,600 feet (488 metres), the longest span in any bridge of its type at that time, and the Manhattan bridge was said to have had the largest carrying capacity of any bridge in the world. The four cables of this bridge could support the weight of two great ocean liners.

British engineers and contractors have also played their full share in the design and construction of the world's bridges. Such great structures as the Forth Bridge and Sydney Harbour Bridge are known by sight to most, as are the older Menai and Saltash bridges which were also great in their day.

But there are many others not known so generally: the great Howrah Cantilever Bridge in Calcutta of 1,500 foot (457 metres) span and the 33 span Lower Zambesi Bridge with a total length of 2½ miles (4 kilometres), for example.

There is a saying that every bridge demands a life. This is not only obviously true when bridges are literally a matter of life and death in war, but also in works of great endeavour. Way back in the mists of recorded history Xerxes the Persian King is known to have beheaded his engineer when his attempt to build a pontoon across the Hellespont was destroyed by storms. The Tay Bridge disaster caused many deaths. The

Quebec bridge fell in 1907 when under construction and carried 82 men to their deaths. When being re-built in 1916 a suspended span broke away and fell with a further 11 men being killed.

There is something indomitable and inspiring about the great bridge builders. A very brief reference to Thomas Telford illustrates the point. At the age of one his father, a shepherd, died and left his widow penniless. She lived in Dumfries and got Thomas apprenticed to a stone mason when he had finished his elementary village schooling. Then a bit of luck came his way. The local landowner, anxious to improve living conditions for his tenants, employed young Thomas on building cottages, bridges, and dams. He managed to fit in extra studies for two years in Edinburgh and then went to London at the age of 25. He worked on Somerset House as a mason. Through his genius for taking pains he gradually rose via being engineer of a canal company to designing what is probably his greatest epitaph—the Menai Suspension Bridge. It was the prototype of all suspension bridges and as precise data was not then available he had each and every link tested to twice the estimated working load. He died still working at the age of 77 and was buried in Westminster Abbey in 1834.

Although it is unlikely to be regarded as making a contribution to the history of bridging I feel I must add an event taking place in 1937, two years before the Germans invaded Poland. It demonstrates one of the many dilemmas which bedevil bridge engineers. It also reveals the delightful eccentricity of the British which inspires against all the odds an occasional and fortuitous breakthrough. Although the latter was not exactly the case in this example, the circumstances command one's admiration for and faith in human frailty and endeavour.

It was in 1937 when Britain started to give some thought to re-arming in the face of growing Nazi aggression in Europe. Finance was then provided for experimenting with new equipment. The tactics of river crossing had to be reviewed in the light of the new tanks and automatic weapons being developed. It was thought by the Generals with unexpected logic that, in order to get the first waves of infantry over the water, some form of boat might be required. So what can only be described as a riotous regatta or at best a version of Henley's rowing championships at their most amateur level took place at the Experimental Bridging Establishment (EBE). No less than 17 types of craft both commercial and individual efforts were demonstrated before an impressive assembly of high-ranking officers.

One chap arrived with an ordinary air-filled mattress which floated very well but he had to be led away gently, biting back his tears, when it was explained that the material was not quite waterproof. Another genius turned up with the complete answer. It was a boat he had invented which, believe it or not, could be carried in a haversack. This was impressive. The prestigious adjudicators watched with considerable interest and high hopes as he unpacked it at the water's edge. An hour later he was still putting it together. It had no less than 37 parts. So, understandably, the verdict, not without respect for his ingenuity, went against him.

And so the day wore more and more wearily on as the various rafts, floats, and boats were unveiled and tested. Things were looking pretty gloomy when the last product was taking to the water as it seemed to be as inadequate as all the others.

Then in a storming finale to the proceedings the hand of Providence produced a trump card. With only five minutes to go before the show was due to end, a lorry was heard screeching to a grinding halt. From it emerged its perspiring occupant with the unlikely name of Mr Goatley of the Saunders Roe Company. He was just in the nick of time to squeeze in his entry in the demonstration. This was a more suitable boat which he had invented. After a hurried and relieved discussion, it was adopted with only a minute to go as the official Assault Boat Mark I.

The logic of using a boat to cross water was thought by some to be very commendable. Then, as now, there was a body of opinion that the men at Whitehall who were alleged to be so busy pinning flags on maps, might easily overlook such a solution. This, of course, is quite unfair. Nevertheless the absence of suitable equipment for crossing the rivers in any reasonable fashion was so acute in the immediate pre-war years that there was a popular assumption about the divinity of the British Army. Without any visible means of support it was thought that all they had to do was to walk on the water.

This somewhat varied and necessarily brief outline of the many-faceted history of bridging needs to be concluded, in order to emphasize the charismatic and shattering importance of having the right bridge at the right time, with the ringing words of Ruskin who said 'Therefore when we build, let us think that we build for ever. Let it not be for present delight, nor for present use alone. Let it be such work as our descendants will thank us for and say, see, this our fathers did for us'.

Donald Bailey did just that, not by building one single bridge destined to perpetuate his name and to serve for generations to come, but by devising a new method whereby thousands of bridges could be rapidly put together, the principles of which ensured that their construction would continue for many decades, indeed for the foreseeable future.

4 The Panel Game

IN late 1940 the vital piece in the jigsaw of re-armament was still missing. What was wanted was a bridge that would enable our forces to help pave the way to ultimate victory. But there was none that could take the loads that would be required. The key links in the battleground and in the logistical chains were not there. Britain's unpreparedness for World War II was only equalled by its unpreparedness for World War I. But in military bridging terms we were more or less starting where we left off in 1918. We were hopelessly behind.

It was an adaptation of the Inglis Bridge, designed in World War I, which, with a pontoon bridge capable of taking only nine tons, was standard equipment. Most of these, if not all, had been lost in France in 1940. In any case the Inglis Bridge which could take a load up to 26 tons, the requirement of a Matilda tank, was soon out-dated. New and much heavier 40-ton tanks like the Churchill were in the pipeline, and with them came a whole new set of criteria for flexible and speedy erection of bridges never before encountered.

It was fortunate indeed that these criteria had been anticipated four years beforehand by Donald Bailey at the Experimental Bridging Establishment (EBE). In 1936 he, together with one Royal Engineer officer, one draughtsman, and a workshop of only 14 men comprised the Establishment. Such shortage of manpower and resources reflected the disastrous policies of the Governments of those days who matched 'appeasement' with opposition to re-armament. It is almost unbelievable, indeed with hindsight agonizingly unbelievable, that at this time there existed a growing file questioning the retention of Donald Bailey on the Establishment on grounds of cost—about £400 p.a.! It comes as a relief to learn that the file was kept pending just long enough for circumstances to change in the light of Hitler's perfidy and aggression. So Donald Bailey did not become redundant. Providence was assuredly on our side because this little band of men inspired by him and later reinforced by a team of wonderfully dedicated and talented people produced the right bridge in the nick of time.

Churchill's immortal tribute to the Battle of Britain pilots that never, in the field of human conflict, was so much owed by so many to so few applies with equal measure to our civil engineer and those who placed their hearts and expertise at the disposal of his revolutionary inspiration. Nothing like it had ever been implemented before and with certain refinements due to the advance of technology and experience it is still in use world-wide to this very day.

When the Inglis Bridge which had been strengthened and adapted to take heavier loads proved unsatisfactory in late 1940, Donald Bailey noted that 'this caused very considerable alarm and despondency in War Office circles for it takes a long time, sometimes a very long time, to get a bridge into production'. In a sense it was a blessing in disguise that the trusty Inglis Bridge could no longer have its usefulness extended. It did not now lend itself to the necessary speed of erection demanded by the pace of mobile war; it had to be built twice as long as the distance needed to bridge the gap because it was swung over the gap on a turntable at the point of balance; it was not easily adapted to take different loads at short notice; and not assembled or dismantled without considerable difficulty under active service conditions.

This was now what seemed to be an insurmountable crisis. Donald Bailey outlined the considerations he had to embrace, each of which posed many problems. Their solution had to be compatible with finding the answers to the other challenges. It was a daunting task. He ticked the points off using the same finger. A bridge was needed in double quick time to carry up to 70-ton loads; to be capable of assembly in different forms so as to be reasonably economic over spans of varying length; to cope with vastly differing loads ranging from the standard army three-ton lorry to tanks of great tonnage and their heavy transporters. Finally it had to have speed of erection and a foolproof design which would enable ordinary soldiers to put it together without mishap.

There were other factors. Due to the speed of erection being the key to success, all parts had to be light and easily fastened together and transported to the site which demanded that all parts must fit easily into standard army lorries and even aircraft. Never before had such criteria been imposed upon a future bridge design. It posed the same absurdity of achievement as asking David to stun Goliath with a meringue in his sling.

It was way back in 1936 when the lone civil engineer at the EBE foresaw where the unexpected future of military bridging might lead. As a consequence he did a few sketches and thought about it intermittently.

He tried on a few occasions, and especially in 1939, to get the powers that be interested in his concept. He told me that 'on two occasions I made an attempt to introduce my ideas to visiting big-wigs from the War Office. I am not going to mention names because it might be hurtful to them and to their relatives, and I am sure they acted with the best of intentions.' He paused for a moment as he searched for the right words which, albeit hesitant and a little slurred, conveyed quite clearly his sense of frustration and his desire to be fair about it all. 'Their reaction depressed me. Although as highly qualified people they should have been the first to appreciate what I was driving at, they did not seem to understand and made little or no attempt to discuss any idea. They left me in no doubt that it was my job to do what I was told and that any personal scheme could only be pursued in my spare time without their backing and certainly not within the precincts of the Establishment.

'Looking back on all this,' he went on, 'I can see that their annoyance with me for putting up what might seem to them a far-fetched diversion was justifiable. They had set their hearts on getting a modified Inglis Bridge off the drawing-board for which they required my entire concentration. Naturally they discouraged any desire on my part to seek an untried alternative.' Thus he was both rejected and dejected. But he still went on working at it in his spare time and became more and more convinced he was on the right track.

At that moment of crisis when he drew the famous outline of his bridge on the back of the envelope he received shortly afterwards a letter from the Ministry of Supply on 14 February 1941 requesting him to carry out a full-scale trial of his complete bridge by 1 May. In other words, virtually from scratch he had to put up the finished job in just over three months when normally it would take a year or even more. But this was not a normal time. By the spirit and dedication of his team and the co-operation of literally thousands of workers all over Britain, many of whom were making parts without even knowing what the bridge was, a miracle was achieved. But that is for the next chapters. Let us first examine the nature of this bridge.

The basic idea is not unrelated to a popular construction game called 'Meccano' which has fascinated children of all ages since the turn of the century. This enables one to screw together standard lengths of flat metal full of little holes. Then, according to the positioning of the screw and angles of the metal pieces, one can assemble replicas of almost anything from bedsteads and wheelbarrows to cranes, engines, robots, and bridges.

It will be appreciated from my elementary example of the plank placed across the stream that if you place a couple of beams alongside both edges to give it support with the help of cross-pieces underneath, then it will be reinforced sufficiently to withstand a given load. In bridging terms these beams are called 'girders'. It follows that if two or more girders are joined together then the strength of the structure can be greatly increased.

But as I have already explained a bridge is not just concerned with the weight it has to carry. It is subject sometimes to extraordinary and sometimes fatal stresses caused, for example, by high winds, by the forces of water whipped to unnatural speed, height and volume by tempest and torrential rain, or by the no less subversive impact of vehicles which, synchronizing with the natural vibration of the bridge's own structure, can grow to breaking point.

With one outstanding idea of devastating simplicity Donald Bailey had thought of something which provided speed, economy, and versatility in bridge building which had never been produced before or bettered since. It met all the requirements already mentioned but which need to be spelled out because it must be remembered that in 1940 and 1941 Britain stood alone against Hitler and if the Nazis were to be defeated a bridge had to be made which would allow mobile warfare to be resumed in Europe.

The vitally important girders supporting the surface over which up to 70-ton loads could be carried had to be capable of being strengthened at will and preferably on the spot. Initially all parts had to be made of readily available metals and to be welded because special steels were almost impossible to obtain at that time. Parts had to be capable of manufacture by almost any engineering firm. This was because all previous bridging equipment had been constrained in output as only a limited number of firms could make it. All parts had to fit into an ordinary standard three-ton lorry so that strange vehicles with prohibitive special bodies and incapable of being replaced at short notice could be dispensed with.

No part should be heavier than a six-man load. This was an amazing innovation which ensured that even under air attack and heavy gun bombardment small six-man teams could get on with the job despite the casualties.

So what was the idea? It was to prefabricate part of a complete girder from top to bottom which would serve for any length of bridge in the form of a panel. This basic unit was five feet (1.5 metres) and 10 feet (3 metres) with two diamond shaped cross braces joining a vertical bar in the middle. The panels could be pinned together end to end to form a girder of any required length so long as it retained sufficient strength to deal with a pre-determined weight of load.

As I have explained, girders joined together increase their capacity for accommodating heavier and heavier loads. A single line of panels formed into a girder could have one or two more lines built alongside so that one had in effect a double single or a triple single. In addition extra singles could be built on top of each other, rising to an erection three storeys high. So seven basic strengths of girder could be furnished at will using combinations of just the one 10 foot by 5 foot (3 x 1.5 metre) panel.

Panel
being carried

Donald Bailey's Bridge was essentially a modular construction. This sketch of six sappers carrying the basic Bailey panel shows how comparatively easy it was to transport. *Harpur*

Other pieces of equipment provided the cross beams between the girders on which the 'road' would rest (called the 'decking'). Structural items to brace against both cross-winds and the shuddering of components due to vehicles changing direction on the bridge were allowed for as part of the all-purpose kit. At the ends of the bridge special pieces which could rock and slide to combat any deflection and/or changes in length due, for example, to temperature variations were also incorporated as part of this astounding 'Meccano' set.

It sounds ridiculous that with all the complications of structure and stress only three basic bits to bind the panels together were needed. They were a panel pin, which was secured in position by a steel safety pin, and a strong chord bolt. The chord is the term used for the 10 foot (3 metre) steel members forming the top and bottom of the panel.

You will recall that with the Inglis Bridge one had to build it more or less parallel to the river or gap and then to a length which would enable it to be swung over on the point of balance. This was a difficult and time-wasting operation because one had to complete the length of bridge needed before it could be put to use as well as building the balancing piece behind it. One also had to find a site with a large enough flat space to allow this to be done.

So our civil engineer piled on his panel inspiration yet another. This accelerated the speed of bridge deployment which saved crucial time. He had his panels assembled on rollers on the home bank, the first part to be put together being of the lightest form possible with the roadway or 'decking' left out. This was called the 'nose'. The bridge proper was built on to this nose and the whole moved gradually forward on rollers as the panels were assembled. Of course care had to be taken to have sufficient weight built behind to prevent the whole bridge tipping forward into the gap. Eventually the nose reached rollers previously ferried to the far side. It then only remained to complete the bridge, to push it forward until in position, to remove the nose, and jack the ends down on to their final foundations. In this way, unlike the Inglis version, the bridge was actually crossing the gap as it was being built.

But let us go back to February 1941 when three significant things had happened. The Experimental Bridging Establishment (EBE) had grown to about 400 personnel with Bailey as its chief designer. His ideas had at last received official approval. The order came down for the bridge to be ready for test by 1 May. The dream of our civil engineer was now about to become a nightmare. He pulled his flat cap well down over his bald head, fastened his sports jacket, pinned his baggy trousers into his clips, and rode home on his bicycle where his wife Phyllis and small son Richard awaited him. He made no mention of the biggest test he had ever been asked to face. In any case he had to go on parade on a night exercise with his Home Guard unit for which he had volunteered at the time of its inception in 1940. Perhaps an unusual incident from that exercise helped to divert his pre-occupation with the vast problems ahead of him. He commanded a section composed entirely of the EBE staff. His task was to defend a local hill against the imaginary enemy.

One of his NCOs was seen to stumble from his trench, and horror of horrors, he then proceeded to flout the black-out regulations by striking match after match. It turned out that in order to fortify himself against the rigours of repelling the non-existent enemy he had downed numerous pints of beer. On arrival at his post he became ill and had lost his false teeth. He practically exhausted all his matches trying to find them. It is not recorded if he did, but it is known that Lieutenant Bailey gave him a stern reprimand (doubtless with a twinkle) and did not reduce the unfortunate NCO to the ranks.

5 The Day Sapper Bloggs Dropped His Spanner

I N the icy gloom of the early mid-winter mornings of 1941 a small saloon car, the product of Standard Motors, would enter the Establishment. The driver was Donald Bailey who, at a time of severe petrol rationing, was given an allowance for which he qualified as one considered to be giving essential service to the war effort. It must have afforded him a certain satisfaction because this privilege was an outward and visible sign of his recognition at long last by his superiors in the various departments of Whitehall.

Bailey could not help reflecting on the irony of it all. He was now being charged with the awesome responsibility of putting his idea into practice, an idea which a few years earlier he had been told to forget as far as any official backing was concerned. When discussing the situation as it then was I asked him to cast his mind back and to tell me how he saw the evolution of his new design which had moved all the way from being a negative reject to a positive project. He gave a wry smile and after what seemed a long interval he said: 'I suppose now I am out of it all I can give a little bit more of my personal feelings, without harm or hurt to anyone. I had spent so much time and thought working on make-and-mend modifications of the Inglis Bridge to provide another version of this trusty old World War I original to meet future loadings needs, that I began to wonder if the next war, which I was sure would be coming, would not provide the same shocks that throughout history our tactics and equipment had suffered at the start of every conflict. We started the Boer War like we finished the Crimean. We started World War I like we finished the Boer War. Here I was actually helping to adapt a World War I bridge to start the next war. It could not be right that history so disastrous should repeat itself.'

When he got to this point I rather rudely interrupted him to ask what he really thought about Inglis who was a Professor at Cambridge University, formerly a sapper Major in World War I, and later to become Sir Charles Inglis. He put me in my place. All he said was: 'Inglis was a friend of mine'.

I prompted him to continue by asking him why he spent all his time working on other people's designs and not on his own ideas: 'That was my job. That was what I was being paid to do. I worked at home on my own ideas, not so much with paper and pen as in my mind. The more I worked on the modifications for existing bridges to take heavier loads, the more the complications arose. At that time we were just about geared with a bit of luck to take the Matilda tank, about 25 tons or so, and although this was a big advance on the old World World I tank of 1918, I felt terribly uneasy about the ability of our bridge capacity to take the heavier tanks which I felt sure would have to replace Matilda. One day I picked up a picture magazine, I think it was called *Picture Post*, and saw a picture of some German army troops. I can't remember the context, but in the background was a tank which looked far heavier and bigger than any I had seen. Perhaps it was my imagination but it frightened me. Then there was the Spanish Civil War and one saw terrible pictures of the destruction caused by aerial bombing. There was that awful debris which would have to be cleared before any bridge could be erected. It did not take much to put two and two together to realize that we had to have a bridge to take far heavier loading than then envisaged and that this bridge had to be easily replaced and flexible in use if it were to be serviceable in a way which would mitigate the effect of bombs dropped by aircraft or if it was hit by shellfire.'

Donald Bailey was not an easy man to interview formally as opposed to having a superficial conventional conversation, because as a victim of his series of strokes his speech was impaired, and having worked for so long as a civil servant in effect in a high security job, his reaction to questions was at first a guarded answer reflecting the wartime admonition that 'careless talk costs lives'. However he always came up eventually with valuable comments and asides and was kind enough to let me have great wads of his hand-written notes and other documents, all very legible because of his very neat rounded writing. 'But how did you get your idea accepted?' I pressed him.

He did not answer for quite some time. I thought he might be finding difficulty in uttering the words he wanted but in fact he was thinking. He was working his way back to what had happened some 42 years previously, a prodigious feat of memory for anyone. Gradually he led me into his story which was amply confirmed and expanded by the talks and interviews he gave after the war which fortunately were on record in the documents he gave to me.

'In the middle 1930s, although it was my job to design bridges, there was not much I could do. In peacetime you do not hear very much about military engineering, not that one heard much about it in wartime either until after D-Day,' he added, with gentle irony. 'Really things were just ticking over and we were playing about mainly on paper with various designs of bridges—some of which, as I said, had been going since World War I or soon after. I knew though that we were coming to the end of the peace and that things were going to hot up a good deal. By the time 1939 came I had this idea for a universal bridge for the army. I made some sketches and submitted them to senior officers who came down to my Establishment. They were polite, but left me in no doubt that nothing would be done to make it official. As a result I could not get the support to go into it properly. I had to put it aside for quite a long time as the main design which was then being considered for the Army was that souped-up version of the World War I bridge already mentioned and which was not liked by the soldiers generally.

'It was when competing bridge designs proved unsatisfactory that once again I resurrected my idea, and was given a little latitude in developing it. But this was before the disappointment of the modified Inglis Bridge and when that was witnessed the "full speed ahead" signal was officially given to my project. In essence mine was the last hope of the powers that be who were now desperate to try almost anything. So you see my idea was never really accepted officially until they had no alternative. There were times when I was very depressed but I was lucky to have the support and encouragement as well as technical advice from Sir Ralph Freeman, the designer of Sydney Harbour Bridge, who was a very influential member of the Structural Engineering Committee set up to advise the Government and War Office about bridging and other equipment.'

When I asked him what his feelings were when he got official permission at last to proceed, he replied 'It was not elation, rather it was a sense of relief that we could get on with the job with the full backing of all those above us. We got the order to have the bridge ready in a matter of a few months for full-scale testing which under normal conditions would be an impossible task. But these were not normal conditions. We were at war with our backs to what we now know to have been a non-existent wall.'

For a succinct and objective description of what now took place I am much indebted to a lengthy article in the *Royal Engineers Journal* of December 1944 which was kindly supplied to me by the author, Lieutenant Colonel S. A. Stewart R.E. (his rank at that time).

Having pointed out that even under demanding wartime conditions it took at least a year for a piece of military equipment to go from the specification stage to delivery to the troops, he highlighted the dilemma which they faced at the end of 1940 in designing a bridge 'for all seasons' which could carry tonnage and have a speed of erection never catered for before. He added 'The solution to the problem was a matter of extreme urgency. The Press has quite correctly reported that this discussion took place in a car on the way back from a meeting held to decide what should be done after the recent failure of some other piece of equipment and the first ideas were in fact discussed over sketches made on the back of an envelope, in an atmosphere of some despondency'.

The idea excited them but nothing could be decided until some sizes and weights could be worked out on paper and these vital calculations were put in hand the very next day. It soon became apparent that a panel of suitable size to get into a 3-ton lorry could be made which would not be too heavy, and that these panels could be made into a girder to take the Churchill tank weighing about 40 tons over a considerable span. This was stupendous news. The telephone rang in Whitehall bringing the triumphant details from Donald Bailey and his team. The decision brooked no delay, and permission was given to go ahead. Having had considerable experience of the shortcomings of earlier equipment it was decided from the outset to eliminate as many of them as possible. It really was a case of more haste, less speed. To avoid the debacle of a bridging innovation which did not take sufficient account of various factors, great care was taken to get the project off to a really good start.

In the early stages almost hourly conferences were held at which first the main features and finally the details were examined from every angle. For several weeks members of the team used to arrive at the office every morning with fresh brain-waves and the best of these were incorporated. Ralph Freeman took a great interest in it from the beginning. To have someone of his experience and calibre behind them was a great bonus. He was consulted frequently and gave the most valuable advice.

As everyone knows, when embarking on a scheme like this, it is essential to have a prototype. But the construction of a pilot model was beyond the capacity of the Experimental Bridging Establishment (EBE) workshops. So the services of a suitable manufacturer were enlisted in order to produce the bulk of the bridge. For this reason, the design of panels and the flooring for the bridge proceeded ahead of the remainder in order to allow the firm to start.

This was a firm called Braithwaite & Company who took the greatest interest in the design, and suggested several features to ease manufacture. They also supplied details of their jigs and welding procedure which were subsequently distributed for the benefit of other manufacturers. As they were made, panels were delivered by road, a dozen at a time, which enabled tests to be started on some of the shorter spans at the earliest possible moment. Great care had to be taken at this stage that all necessary fittings were incorporated in the panel and that no subsequent alterations were made which would delay production. The remaining items were designed one by one and manufactured in EBE workshops.

In contrast with the year or more normally taken to put a new piece of equipment into production, the time taken in this instance was just a matter of months. Design and production of the pilot model proceeded concurrently and it was in fact ready for test in four and a half months and production was under way in seven months. For such a major item of equipment, these times were quite exceptional. Luck undoubtedly played its part, but the sense of urgency and purpose consumed everyone on the job. The adrenalin never flowed faster. In the drawing office, the nerve centre of the operation, it was not unusual for the designer and draughtsmen to work for 16 hours on the trot and then take their work home with them for the other eight as their sub-conscious minds improved their efforts in their sleep.

Owing to the novel nature of the structure, it was decided that all calculations should be checked by more than usually exhaustive tests and further, that such tests should be carried out to destruction. The ultimate breaking point had to be established to allow the parameter of safety for varying loads to be laid down.

The bridge was accordingly erected on a flat field, about two feet (0.6 metres) clear of the ground, so that jacks and safety packing could be arranged underneath. All test loads were applied statically. Jacks with long handles for leverage were placed under the centre of the span to hold the bridge until the load was in place; then they were slacked off, just as one jacks up a motor car to change a tyre and then releases it when the new tyre is in place. The static load included an extra allowance for stress caused by vehicle impact and other causes. In addition this extraordinary dead weight was not put in the most favourable position for bearing it, that is in the centre, but was applied up against one kerb at an angle of maximum eccentricity. Only by this means could an accurate assessment of the stresses on the various parts of the bridge be made.

The actual arrangement of some of the test loads would have filled a laboratory man with horror. For various reasons it was necessary to apply a considerably greater load to one particular span than had ever been done by the EBE before, and the application of this load, to an area of deck 12 feet (3.65 metres) long, presented certain problems of its own.

The main problem was one which a layman would hardly envisage. But if one is going to place a load, which is heavier by many tons than anything experienced before, on a given piece of raised roadway where and how does one find the tonnage? Furthermore, if and when found, how does one plonk it on the bridge if there are no cranes able or available to help? The genius of the EBE team for improvisation found a remarkable answer. It was actually achieved by driving an old 1917 Mark V tank on to the centre of the bridge. A scissors bridge was then placed as a ramp up the back of the Mark V tank and a timber platform erected at the top of it. On this, two additional tanks were poised, one in front of the other on the top of the Mark V. 'Poised' is the correct word. The Mark V was further filled with pig iron and some tons of heavy scrap were also added to the heap wherever room could be found for them. A photograph taken at the time clearly shows this extraordinary pyramid.

On one occasion, when demonstrating the bridge under test before the Structural Engineering Committee, the Bailey team was feeling a little uneasy about showing such a crude arrangement before such a distinguished scientific body. This embarrassment was increased by a light shower of rain which wetted the surface of the scissors bridge just sufficiently to prevent one of the upper tanks from climbing it. It was finally accomplished with the assistance of a large gang of men heaving on a rope. They tried to get the Committee to look the other way while all this was going on but obviously fascinated by such departures from the text books, they would not do so. Fortunately when the jacks were lowered away from under the bridge, it successfully withstood the load.

On another occasion a test caused considerable concern. The prestigious Structural Engineering Committee was once more in attendance and the intention was to load a bridge successfully with gradually increasing overloads until a point was reached, just before failure. This had been decided upon as the load necessary to pass the bridge. Tests had by this time reached such a point that one more success would have ensured acceptance of the design, so this was the final and crucial one. Owing to the crude methods it took nearly all day and the final overload could not be applied until about 6 p.m. Many of the Committee were in fact temporarily away from the site at which they had spent many weary hours.

The men on the jacks supporting the centre of the span slacked off and finally reported all clear, but just before taking essential measurements one jack-man said 'Just a minute, sir. I've still got a little load'. This meant he could not pull his jack clear. He slacked off, but the load still remained. The hopes of the team, which had been soaring after each successful test up to this one, received a sickening blow. So much work under so much stress had been achieved. Just when they were counting on the solution to the victory bridge being proven beyond doubt, one man on one jack had ruined it. Numbed by it all, and fearing the worst, they set about examining the parts. Eventually they saw what had happened. The top part on one side of the bridge had failed by buckling, but so gently that no one had noticed it.

The Committee was hastily collected and a close examination of the damaged panel was made. A new clue gave new hope. One side of the top part had a bad scar, where it had evidently been struck by a tank in an earlier test. This, coupled with the severe overload, had been sufficient to cause failure. At this discovery the designers breathed a sign of relief, and men were put on to work throughout the night to replace the damaged panel. Rooms were booked for the Committee at the local hotel.

Next morning the test was ready to be re-enacted. One can imagine the tension of the team for whom this was the climax of all the preceding brainwork and sweat.

During the previous months they had striven by might and main, by night and day, by all that they held dear, to get the Bailey perfected. A team of about a dozen or so key people now regarded it not so much a bridge as a crusade. Problems, problems, problems, were met with answers, answers, and more answers. Tests followed tests. Adjustments, modifications, and different drills for the sappers all evolved in a happy pattern of positive progress. But now new and hideous doubts had come.

One can reasonably assume that in the stress of the conclusive test that morning to determine the fraction of weight before the bridge's breaking point was reached, the number of seconds it took to ease off the last jack was the same fraction of time before the breaking point of the team was reached. With an anxiety which no words can describe they must have watched the jacks being lowered allowing the bridge to carry alone the burden of its vast tonnage. As if sustained in part by the power of the silent prayers offered by the spectators, the bridge never budged. All the jacks were clear. The bridge, with its new panel replacing the damaged one, had met the challenge with just a hint perhaps of the reassurance which it conveyed in combat in the years that lay ahead.

The team breathed again in triumph. They now faced the daunting dilemma of getting sufficient quantities of their bridge to those waiting in Britain to train with and above all to our Allies in North Africa to fight with.

While the one just described was the last great test of the Bailey in peace-time conditions, it is appropriate, at the risk of slight duplication, to describe the genesis of the operation and the first test in the words of the inventor of this revolutionary bridge. He said it all in a few hundred words shortly after the war when addressing his local Rotary Club. For understatement, and at the same time for producing an unforgettable climax, it could hardly be better or more modestly summarized. After describing his earlier career he went on: 'Then came 1940 and the fall of France—Dunkirk. The times were not altogether propitious, but the plans were even then being made for our return to the Continent, and we should require—amongst a host of other equipment—a bridge which would carry our tanks, guns, and lorries over the rivers of France, Belgium, and Holland into Germany. They must carry bigger and better tanks, too, than any we had at that time—a volume of traffic undreamed of.

'I unearthed my old idea and worked on it again—it seemed to fulfil the War Office requirements, but there were rival designs in the field which had had some trial. However, good friends thought that there was sufficient promise to justify completion of the design, and the project was given official standing. This meant all the resources of the Establishment were made available.

'Hardly had this been done when — on 14 February 1941 — a letter was received from London ordering us to be ready to carry out a full-scale trial of a complete bridge by May. The task was a tremendous one. The production drawings had to be made, the steel rolled, jigs for manufacture thought out and fabricated. We knew that we could rely on our own men to pull their full weight, and more, but it is not always so easy to instil a sense of urgency into those outside who had now to be brought in.

'So whilst our drawing office worked far into the nights to produce the drawings, strings were pulled to ensure prompt rolling of the steel and I myself journeyed to the Midlands to visit a firm who were said to have the capacity for manufacture.

'After examining the draft drawings, the firm agreed to undertake the work and to start making the necessary jigs immediately. This they did, and, to cut a long story short, eventually delivered the main steelwork on 1 May. For our own shops had, in the meantime, made up the remaining smaller parts and a local firm had made up about 30 feet (9 metres) of bridge girders from a cheaper quality of steel, in order that we might carry out destructive tests to settle one or two hotly debated points in connection with this rather unusual type of construction. These fully justified our claims.

'At length the great day arrived when the bridge was to be demonstrated to the War Office. We had only just received the girders and, as a result of the haste in manufacture, all sorts of adjustments had to be made at the last moment. However, after a hectic all-night session by our workshops we found that we had an hour or so to spare in the morning before the great men were due to arrive, in which the Royal Engineers who were to erect the bridge could get in a little practice. This was extended to about two hours owing to a blitz in London the previous night which made the train late and, incidentally, did not improve the tempers of the visitors. We did what we could with sandwiches and beer to smooth their tempers down, but wished we had laid on a proper lunch. But it was too late to do anything now, and we could only hope that the sappers would put up a good show.

'At two o'clock the Officer in charge of the erection party ordered "In double time form bridge". He blew his whistle and they were off. To our anxious eyes how slow everything seemed. The delays were endless. Sapper Bloggs had dropped a spanner and couldn't find it. Eventually the bridge was completed and a lorry rumbled across my bridge for the first time. We looked at our watches — we had not dared to do so before. It was 2.36. Surely there must be some mistake — but no, there wasn't. The 70 foot (21 metre) bridge had been completed in 36 minutes.

'The bridge was adopted. Then started the building of the huge organization which was to be responsible for arranging the manufacture, testing, inspection, and provision of materials.'

A magazine article written a few years after the end of World War II, when the lapse of time enabled this project to be put in a more objective context, named it 'one of the most brilliant individual inventions of the war'. It drew attention to the fact also, not mentioned before, that each panel, including all its little bits and pieces, consisted of no more than 17 parts and that the sections could be joined together with comparatively little noise, a vital point when construction was often done within earshot of the enemy. Emphasizing the small number of parts the article stated that, 'The best that the Germans could do was to produce a bridge, nothing like as strong or simple, which apart from the numerous main components required 24 nuts and bolts alone for each section'.

Two letters I received throw interesting light on some of the problems Donald Bailey faced when developing his prototype. It will be recalled that, in putting the prototype to its most exacting test, the team's ingenuity solved the difficulty of finding enough tonnage to impose upon the bridge. This they did by trundling a Mark V 1917 tank on to the centre and then by further improvised ramps they hoisted two smaller tanks on top of it. They rounded off this Heath-Robinson-type jumble by cramming pig iron inside the old Mark V tank and adding tons of steel beams wherever possible. But how could the team *prove* to the War Office, the Ministry of Supply, and to the Structural Engineering Committee that the resultant tonnage was authentic. Well, one vital clue is provided by a letter from Mr E. S. Davies of Bournemouth: 'When I was about 18 in the early 1940s I was answering the telephone in the railway Goods Office at Bournemouth Central Station when there was a call from someone at the Experimental Establishment, Barrack Road, Christchurch, asking the capacity of the weighbridge in the Goods Yard. When I told him he said he would like to send along an army tank to be weighed and get an official ticket to convince people in London. He told me that they had designed and made a portable bridge but London doubted whether it would be strong enough to take the weight of a tank. So they sent a photo of one on the bridge and had a reply that there must be a mistake about the weight of the tank. Next day it came into the yard and was weighed. As it was dealt with by the Yard Foreman, Charlie Fairweather, I heard no more about it but hope London was convinced. The caller may have been Mr Bailey, as he then was.'

A letter from Mrs Kerley from Christchurch told me that her father, a member of the EBE, was with Donald Bailey in a car coming back from a meeting in London. Donald was still worrying about the design of the panel pins. Her father emptied his packet of cigarettes and together, using the empty carton, they apparently worked it out. This has sufficient resemblance to Bailey's famous back-of-the-envelope bridge design which he also demonstrated in the back of a car to make one wonder if he was particularly receptive to inspiration as a passenger in a motor vehicle.

Miss Elvin, then aged 16, who with her father was also working at EBE helping with the original scale drawings of the bridge, vividly recalls it all. She is now living in America and I wrote to her in her married name of Mrs Leland Batchelder in Idaho. Her reply produced a nugget of human interest and suggested that the Bailey bridge was of feminine gender.

'I was pleased to get your letter' she said 'about the Grand Old Lady, as we affectionately called the Bailey Bridge'. Mrs Batchelder then described how when the first 30 foot (9 metre) span was laid out on the bridging field the Germans helped to test it! It had been arranged for the RAF to strafe the bridge to see how it stood up to it. However before they arrived the air raid sirens went, everyone dived for cover, and two German fighter planes spotted the bridge and dived on it repeatedly with guns blazing.

'The Germans did a really good job' she said, without revealing the damage done because she switched her anecdote to the shock she had when the 'all clear' came. Her father was missing and panic ensued. Then someone shouted 'Here he is'. He had knocked himself out when he hit his head against the large gun of a tank when emerging from its cover. At first it was thought he had been hit by a bullet, but all was well. She concluded with an enthusiastic tribute to the brotherhood of the Bailey. 'Rarely can there have been such a large number who worked so hard together to get that bridge erected. We were all so proud of HER. . . .'

Having proved that his bridge was the answer, Donald Bailey faced in some respects a more daunting task. 'I felt really dispirited,' he said, 'because after the high of the successful tests came the low point of finding ways and means whereby it could go into mass production. Everybody in Britain was already working on something else of national importance. Materials were scarce. It was a problem. A big problem.'

6 The Great Gamble

THE most widely circulated reading matter at that time apart from the Bible, and certainly the most scanned, was the ration book. Every member of every household was issued with one. They were more precious than passports. Their possession entitled families to receive tiny amounts of everyday necessities such as butter, sugar, tea, meat, cheese, and bacon. They were a constant reminder of Britain's fight to feed itself and its precarious dependence on food convoys crossing the hostile seas. In addition the nation was urged to 'Dig for Victory' so that home-grown vegetables could supplement the meagre fare. All the cinemas carried advertising paid for by the Ministry of Food suggesting tasty but economical recipes. Strange new items enlivened the gastronomic range such as powdered egg, a composite pork delicacy called 'Spam', and 'Snoek', masquerading as a fish steak.

Other consumer goods were strictly rationed. Coupons had to be presented to get a few ounces of sweets. Clothing coupons were issued without which one could not get any fabrics or dress material. Petrol coupons were traded on the Black Market at a high premium. Even the furniture was reduced to essentials like bedsteads, tables, and chairs. They were of such simple design and attained such minimal standards that they were described officially under the generic label of 'Utility'.

The public were not only urged to 'Dig for Victory' but also to invest in War Bonds, to save scrap metal, to donate aluminium saucepans, to hoard scrap paper, to cut down railings for collection, and above all to 'Keep Mum' as careless talk about troop movements, for example, might cost lives.

There was also a mandatory personal contribution to the war effort which affected everyone. Hundreds of thousands of men and women, running eventually into millions, were called up in various age groups if they had not already volunteered. They were then allocated to the three armed Services or to essential jobs in industry and agriculture to keep supplies at the highest pitch. Indeed so important was the raw material and factory production that in the early stages men with suitable experience who had been directed to the forces were demobilized and returned to civilian duties. Afterwards more and more women took over the skilled jobs in factories, and down on the farms Britain's Land Girls, sporting their official-issue heavy green knickers, wielded fork and spade to great effect. Thus many men were released for front-line fighting, all that is except for the miners. To get enough coal a number of young men who were called up were offered the alternative of going down the pits instead of into one of the three Services. Those who accepted were dubbed 'Bevin Boys' after Ernest Bevin, the Minister of Labour in Churchill's Government.

So great was the civilian war effort, so labour-intensive, so well planned, that practically the entire population was at action-stations on shift work of national importance. It was calculated that behind every soldier in battle there were no less than seven people on the home front producing what he needed.

Against this background of austerity and regimentation Donald Bailey and his team faced the awesome problem of how to get mass production of all the parts of their bridge when the skilled workers of the nation were already employed in the mass production of everything else needed to meet the voracious demands of a total war effort. Thousands of people would have to be found to produce sufficient bridging in time to make victory possible. But where were they to come from? Certainly not from the munitions factories, nor the mines, nor the agricultural areas, nor the aviation industry, nor from the vehicle assembly lines, nor from the host of those companies already sub-contracted to produce the cogs, plugs, washers, and the myriad mechanical mites ranging from pins to ball bearings without which little can function.

So they decided on a great gamble. This was to tap sources of unskilled workers, so far untouched, in the hope that somehow they would learn how to do the job and to produce the goods. The only answer was to turn to those versatile but untrained reservoirs of labour represented by girls, housewives, and any reasonably able-bodied men too old for active service, who all found employment of some kind or another in service, leisure, or fringe manufacturing businesses. It was unbelievable but in a matter of months from 1941 onwards thousands and thousands among these groups of workers were making all the bits that made up the Bailey Bridge. Firms that made bedsteads, greenhouses, window frames, canoe paddles, combined with paper makers, garages, mail order businesses, confectioners, football pool proprietors, and even restaurateurs, to provide the labour for what must have been one of the greatest mass-production success stories of all time.

It was a miracle of imagination, organization, and motivation. Every part had to be made very accurately, especially the panel holes and pins as each part had to be reliably inter-changeable to a minute fraction of an inch. So each unit of workforce was given precision prototypes of the pieces they were making to copy. Experts in each facet of manufacture initially supervised and instructed the ladies whose mechanical knowledge had never gone further than recognizing a screwdriver or opening a tin of sardines.

At the beginning there was a surge of production but understandably it fell off badly because of the boring and repetitive nature of a job which by itself could not be identified with the war effort. However when it was explained, and here General Montgomery as he then was played his part, that what they were making was a vital part of the guts of a bridge urgently needed to keep the Allied armies moving, production leaped again and never flagged.

The stories are endless of the heroic harmony of the sappers and the workers and their beloved 'Bailey'. Kind editors of various newspapers published a letter from me requesting anecdotes for this book and the response came in scores of letters from all over the country. They typify the dedication of probably the weirdest combination and certainly the most diversified of any work force contributing to a single project.

Mrs Elsie Labrum in Dorset wrote: 'As I was welding Bailey Bridges during part of the last war, one of the fitters with whom I worked at that time gave me two pages of *The Sphere* of July 1944 about the Bailey Bridge which you may care to borrow' (I did). 'I would like to see the book on completion as, apart from myself, I correspond with an ex-Bailey-Bridge welder in Canada.'

This letter emphasizes the fact that thousands of ordinary people including the wonderful women who turned their hand to every job to release man-power for the forces, were involved in making the panels and other components. Her casual remark about her Canadian counterpart confirms the international nature of the Bailey workers.

The importance of the women's role is further demonstrated with these words from Mrs Constance Watts: 'Through this period I worked at a photoprint office in Cambridge and we printed many drawings brought to us by the boffins. In those days it was all very secret and I would add that life was very serious and that there was little of a frivolous nature. We worked a 12- or 18-hour day when the necessity arose without com-plaining and little remuneration. We considered it a privilege to help our country which was then in dire distress.'

Mrs Pearce of Torquay adds more authority to the diversification and dedication of the women workers: 'I was at the British Cellophane factory in Bridgewater from December 1941—March 1945. We made the Bailey

Bridge. My contribution consisted of the pins that held them together. I had five separate saws which were set to the required length of the pins. We were on piece work. Day shift 8 a.m. to 8 p.m. Night shift 8 p.m. to 6 a.m. I had to punch every pin on the end with my own number. The welders were mostly London men who had made their homes in Bridgewater to get away from the blitz. We had to *work* to earn the money, but we were a happy band.'

Mrs Lily Smith wrote from Birmingham: 'The only thing I had ever been good at was knitting. So you can imagine what a shock it was to find myself unravelling the welding equipment and trying my hand at fusing the panel joints. We went to the local garage for training and there we met others in our team who remained life-long friends. One day my special pal, Katie, nearly burnt me to death when she swiveled around unexpectedly with her blow-lamp. Actually she only singed my overall slightly and we had a good laugh!'

As soon as the bridge was formally accepted for production, a large number of firms had been forewarned to stand by for a rush job, and orders for materials had been placed well in advance. Thus within five months of production being put in hand the first bridges were with the troops. Furthermore during the early stages of production, vehicle-loading trials, launching trials, and troop trials were held so that construction drills could be finalized for the issue of a provisional user handbook. How about that? For a nation noted for 'muddling through' this piece of brilliant foresight and planning must have been very worrying for the enemy.

A brilliant example was set by Littlewoods, the famous football pools and chain store firm and probably the best known name in Britain for the millions who filled in weekly coupons in the hope of winning a fortune by forecasting the results of football matches. The contribution of this firm to Bailey bridging was to make the pontoons on which it could be floated across the widest rivers. This was a vital consideration which was tackled concurrently with the manufacture of the panels. The means whereby the bridge could be used were deemed to be as important as the bridge itself.

Littlewoods represented a triumph of organization and initiative. Apart from pontoons, they made shells, fuses, frames for Wellington bombers, dinghies, barrage balloons, storm boats, and no less than five and a half million parachutes—their first assignment. At the outbreak of war, they placed their vast organization at the service of the nation, and subsequently developed into one of the most versatile cogs in Britain's war machine. Buildings and factories which had been the homes of pools, mail order business, and chain store administration were absorbed into one high-powered drive to produce the weapons the country needed. Where there were factories they were reconditioned and placed into war production. Where there were no factories, buildings were taken over.

In the space of years the organization grew to such an extent that, whereas in September 1939, the Littlewoods war effort began with one pools building given over to His Majesty's Censorship, and another building requisitioned for the launching of the first products—parachutes—by the end of 1944 there were over 16 factories laid out and equipped in the most up-to-date style, working at full pressure, and employing a total of over 14,000 workpeople, predominantly women. Between the peacetime organization of pools, mail-order trading, and chain stores, and the war-time manufacture of parachutes, balloons, pontoons for Bailey bridges, shells, and aircraft, there would appear to have been no common ground. But Littlewoods' wartime record proved beyond question that previous experience in any task was far from being a first essential in the successful prosecution of that task. If real organizing ability is there, if keenness, sound judgment, initiative, and drive are possessed by the executive staff, if the workpeople are united by esprit-de-corps and pride of corporate achievement, then there is practically no limit to what can be achieved.

Littlewoods, like so many other companies both big and small, demonstrated that general administration and executive experience was far more important than technical experience. Workpeople could be trained to do entirely new tasks in a matter of weeks and very often the absence of technical traditions and ready-made routine were found to inspire initiative and to encourage the discovery of new methods and more efficient solutions to the problems that arose.

By 1943 more and more organizations were drawn speedily into the mystique of Bailey Bridge production. Eventually 650 firms from all over the United Kingdom were involved, and with so much inexperienced labour it was decided to test all the panels to be certain that they were up to the required standard. So testing centres were set up at which all panels were added one by one to form a continuous girder. As one panel was added the one at the end was taken off. However when production soared to 25,000 panels a month random testing had to be introduced for a time until special machines were introduced to enable 100 per cent testing to be resumed. It stands as indelible evidence of the incredible efficiency of this operation that less than 300 panels were rejected of the hundreds of thousands made.

So to summarize the time span of this achievement which normally would take a good deal longer working under normal conditions: design work started in December 1940, the prototype was ready for trial in May 1941, production started in July 1941, and the first parts were leaving the factories by December 1941—just a year from concept to finished product.

From 1942 to 1945 nearly half a million tons of Bailey bridging were made for use in every theatre of war. This included no less than 700,000 panels which, if laid end to end, as the cliché goes, would stretch from London to Leningrad.

One final problem, just to show how an obscure obstacle can arise, and equally to demonstrate how the solution to it can be brilliantly and simply devised, was related to steel. It was necessary in a foolproof manner to distinguish the special steel which was eventually produced for the Bailey Bridge from the ordinary run-of-the-mill stuff. So a broad green line was painted down the middle for the Bailey sections. However, this was followed by the welding of the steel becoming cracked. The detective work that followed defies description in layman's terms but the cause was tracked down to sulphur in the paint having an adverse effect on the weld. So by simply substituting an oil-bound distemper free of sulphur the trouble was avoided.

One's preoccupation with the nuts and bolts of bridges must not be allowed to displace the very human story of the forgotten man after whom more bridges have been named than anyone else in the world. At least 2,500 were built in the Italian campaign alone. Another 2,000 in north-west Europe and in the Far East. Hundreds more were built after the war. Improved versions of it are still in use all over the world.

It is hard to believe that the vast amount of publicity which surrounded the disclosure of Donald Bailey's name in 1944 would even after the lapse of years have permitted his memory to fade.

7 The Mystery Man from the Ministry

AS I look at the scores of massive headlines and lengthy stories in countless press cuttings of 1944 and 1945 in front of me, I am very conscious how, at a time of acute newsprint rationing in Britain, so much space was given to publicize the inventor and the bridge named after him. The enthusiastic editorial comment and speculation went overboard in the realization that without the bridge there might be no end to the war.

The first inklings, before the official press releases which came months later, that something very sensational in the way of Allied war effort had arrived, broke in various newspapers early in 1944. Then, through lack of background information, reports were played down to only three or four column inches. The most provocative one to set the world guessing came from a Sunday newspaper dated 13 February 1944. It was a most intriguing and prophetic story. It started off with a headline in black boldface type posing the question so many of the Allied soldiers were asking:

'WHO IS BAILEY?'

It added in a sub-headline 'A name famous throughout Italy'. The story continued . . . 'Everywhere in Italy you heard the soldiers say "This man Bailey is a marvel. If any man deserves a VC, he does. He has done the greatest job in this war."

But who is Bailey? Nobody in Italy knows, although his name is as famous as Montgomery's and everyone there knows what he has done. Nobody ever seems to have seen him. His identity is one of the most discussed topics of the Army. Some say he is a soldier, some say he is a civil servant, some say he is a civilian outside of all the Services.'

Here followed a break in the story with a bold sub heading of 'HUSH

HUSH' and then it continued: 'Some say he is rich, some poor. Some tell you what he has done in Italy must, and indeed ought to, have made him rich. Others say, in the cynical way of soldiers, "Well, I expect that all he got was a rise of £5 a year." Now what Mr Bailey has done is still very hush-hush, except to the Army. And it may be that even Mr Bailey himself does not know how famous he is in Italy.'

The report continued with a note of reassurance: 'He does exist. He works in a Ministry in Britain *and one day when his story is told it will be one of the finest chapters ever told of British inventive genius.*' The italics in the last sentence are mine. They need no elaboration.

In confirmation of this newspaper report I felt I should add a remark by one Corporal Dodwell, a company clerk in my regiment. His previous military experience was gained in London's wartime night club 'The 400' where each night he was, as they say 'loaded'. Although several ranks above him in status, I always felt privileged to serve under him. He was busy tapping out something on his typewriter, sitting on the back of his office truck, and in his pending tray were filed a bottle of vino and a half-eaten sandwich which the Army cherished as the 'unexpired portion of the day's rations' or UXPDR for short. As I approached him he moved his cigarette heavy with ash from one side of his mouth to the other to signal his appreciation of my presence. Then suddenly two loud explosions with long columns of vertical smoke took our attention as the Germans blew their bridges about half a mile away. Corporal Dodwell turned to his field telephone, picked up a receiver, and said authoritatively to his imaginary subordinate: 'This is Dodwell here. Send for Mr Bailey!'

But a day after the first newspaper story about the unknown Mr Bailey appeared, the secret was out at last. The identity of the mystery man from the Ministry was confirmed. A daily newspaper with a headline going across three quarters of its page printed: 'THIS IS THE BAILEY THE ARMY PRAISES' and the report with an introduction in heavy type continued: 'Donald Coleman Bailey, aged 42, married, one child, civil engineer, living on the outskirts of a South Coast town, who has not yet been out of England since the war began, realized yesterday that he is famous among troops overseas. Yesterday this slim tall man with thinning hair and cheerful youthful face said "I'm glad the fighting men like my bridges"'. The story was then padded out with trivia because, as Donald Bailey said, 'it is still all pretty secret'. Ten days later a story in the *New York Herald Tribune* told more. It had two headings 'BAILEY BRIDGE ON LIST OF INVASION WEAPONS' and 'LIKENED TO HUGE MECCANO SET IT SPANS RIVER CROSSINGS.' The report then went on to say that 'One of the important pieces of equipment which the Allied invasion forces here will take with them to the Continent will be the "Bailey Bridge"—a building development used for the first time in Allied operations in North Africa and hitherto on the "secret" list. In North Africa sappers became efficient at hooking the bridge—which has been likened to a huge Meccano set—together and making a causeway over a river that would carry tanks.

'In Sicily and in Italy the Allied forces used the bridge to excellent advantage but its name and construction still remained secret. Now it can be revealed that it is the invention of Donald Coleman Bailey, 42-year-old civil engineer, who lives in Southbourne on England's south coast.'

It was not until after the D-Day landings mentioned in this report that the newspaper and periodical Press in most of the free countries of the world were permitted by British censorship to tell their readers the dramatic story of the Bailey Bridge in words and for the first time in pictures. Their acclaim in recognition of the invention can be summarized in the enormous headlines and enthusiastic comments which went on month after month. These few examples are typical:–

The *Daily Sketch* of 26 June 1944 devoted the whole of its centre page spread to spectacular photographs of the bridge in use in Italy. The heading was:

'FIRST PICTURES TO SHOW HOW THE BAILEY BRIDGE WINS THE BATTLE OF DEMOLITIONS'

'Sappers in action with the famous Bailey Bridge'.

The *Sphere* periodical claimed to have first pictures in its 1 July issue 1944 with the introduction 'The Bailey Bridge—the answer to German demolitions' and then goes on to quote General Montgomery, as he then was, who said the bridge was 'Quite the best thing we have ever had.'

In September 1944 the *Sunday Mercury* carried a long article boldly headlined 'Wonderful Bailey Bridge' and listed about half-a-dozen advantages it had over the German bridging equipment.

Another periodical at the same time pictured Donald Bailey chatting to a sapper beside one of his bridges and the caption included the following tributes:

'TRIUMPH OF THE BAILEY BRIDGE—the story of a British genius who, in a moment of dire emergency and against almost impossible odds, produced one of the most brilliant inventions of our time.

'The Bailey Bridge, one of the greatest wartime inventions, also holds unlimited peacetime possibilities.' These last words, as subsequent chapters will show, were completely justified. Another phrase in this magazine article was a striking appreciation. 'It is one of the few flawless inventions of the war.'

The *Daily Mirror* on 26 June 1944 splashed the story in boldface type: 'WONDER BRIDGE SECRET IS OUT'.

The text went on at length to explain how the bridge came about, how it was operated with such success in all theatres of war, and it added a little human touch with: 'The inventor, Mr Donald Bailey of the Ministry of Supply, who told last night of its development would not disclose what special metal was used but said "we don't like park railings".'

It is interesting to compare the similarity of assessment and praise of Lt General H. G. Martin writing in the *Daily Telegraph* about the role of the engineers of the Allied Armies in Italy before D-Day and of the anonymous but equally distinguished writer in *The Times* ('our special correspondent at SHAEF') writing about 'The Storming of the Rhine!'

To emphasize the nature of the demolitions carried out by the Germans and the vital value of the Bailey bridge it is necessary to quote Lt General Martin at some length: 'As one surveys the multifarious activities of the Engineers in Italy—activities all-important to the Allied cause—one is apt to conclude that this is above all an engineer's war. It is undoubtedly true that in no prior campaign have the Engineers made so large a contribution to victory—if for no other reason than that in no prior campaign have we fought an enemy who has indulged in demolition on so vast a scale and in a terrain so perfectly adapted to it.

'As the front moved northward, demolitions increased accordingly, till, about the line Foggia-Naples, he [Jerry] began his crowning orgy of destruction.

'In this area immediately behind the present front the extent of these demolitions has to be seen to be believed. Throughout this land of mountain, gorge, and river the enemy has blown almost every bridge and every culvert—on roads and railways both. There was, for instance, a long viaduct near Isernia where the railway crossed a gorge on perhaps a dozen masonry piers. The Germans had not been content with just blowing a gap in this viaduct; no, with infinite labour they had set themselves utterly to destroy every single pier.

'Again, there were whole sections of the railway along which the German wrecker-train had passed; there, mile on mile, every sleeper had been uprooted and smashed; every rail first cut, and then tossed aside—an acme of destruction which they achieved with the minimum of effort by the simple expedient of dragging a grapnel behind the wrecker-train in order to destroy the sleepers, while the Germans themselves sat at ease and fed into a couple of hoppers twin streams of small explosive charges fitted with time-fuses and magnets, which drop down and adhere to the rails.

'Before our Armies could move—before they could even be supplied—the Engineers had to repair a sufficiency of routes through this maze of destruction. *And here we may thank our stars for one of the really great inventions of the war, to wit, the Bailey bridge.* Standardized and adaptable to almost any load, it is the product of the Royal Engineers' Experimental Bridging School, after one of whose professors it has been named and it was first used at Medjez el Bab in the Tunisian campaign.

'Thus it is a home-made product reckoned greatly superior to any military bridge as yet produced by any other army, Red or otherwise. In fact I am told that a Russian observer on the Italian front, having seen the nature of the enemy's defence,

admitted frankly that, lacking the Bailey bridge, no Russian army could have got so far—and that you will agree was a considerable admission.'

The Times' article referred to the storming of the Rhine as a 'landmark in modern river warfare' and succinctly referred to the importance of the Bailey Bridge:

'The military engineers who, on the Rhine, are surpassing even their great record of achievement, have not lacked experience in handling the wealth of bridging material with which the modern army is equipped, for though the Germans have sometimes been stampeded into leaving a vital bridge intact—Nijmegen and Remagen are the outstanding examples—their demolition technique has been most thorough. Field Marshal Montgomery's 21st Army Group alone has constructed more than 1,000 Bailey bridges during its advance—*and when one speaks of the Bailey bridge, there in a nutshell is the answer to most river problems. This admirable British invention, widely adopted by the American armies, was most carefully thought out before being issued and has stood the test of every type of crossing.* Its neat simple sections, in which every bit of steel is doing its duty, have almost limitless possibilities. But perhaps its main virtue is that the sappers like it.'

Naturally by now Mr Bailey and his Bridge had become so famous that the master of witty and elegant doggerel in his time, Mr A.P. Herbert, had this to say:

THE BRIDGE
There's always some new river in the way
(I like to think that rivers matter still).
Always the bridge was broken yesterday;
And panting hosts are thwarted of their kill.
But patience, tank—stand back, you saucy Jeeps!
We have a wizard all the world must clap.
Over the stream our Mr Bailey leaps
And leaves his monument on every map.

Illingworth, the famous *Daily Mail* cartoonist, did a humorous montage of thumbnail sketches depicting many things the British supplied to aid the war effort. It included a drawing of a jeep speeding over a bridge. The driver is saying 'Wasn't it lucky Mrs Bailey had such a clever son.'

In a series of wartime cartoons on the theme 'Smiling Through' by Lee in the *London Evening News*, there was another mention. It showed a couple wading through the floods to their water-logged home and speculating 'It's a nice little cottage, and if we can only get a Bailey Bridge from Army Surplus after the war. . . .'

But the cartoon which gave Donald Bailey most personal pleasure was one which dramatized the speed of erection of his bridge. He recounted it in his own words:

'In spite of many difficulties, bridges were completed at a rate which rarely failed to take the enemy by surprise and I think can be aptly summed up by a small cartoon I saw. This depicted a long bridge, miles long, disappearing way off over the horizon. In the foreground was a young officer saluting his senior and saying "the bridge is now ready for traffic—Sir" to which the senior officer replied "Damn it, I should think so, you've been on the job all morning." '

But the eulogy of Bailey and his Bridge was not confined to the cartoon or written word. It is thanks to the written word that we know from an article in *The Listener* dated 3 August 1944 the full account given in a major BBC Radio broadcast by William Holt. Although it is very slightly technical, it is expressed so simply and clearly and in such terms that, having read this far, the reader will be able to savour and appreciate even more the amazing impact and versatility of this invention. I propose to reproduce it here word for word. Anybody who has not by now fully grasped the significance of the Bailey Bridge, and there are many like myself who cannot grasp a spanner, let alone a revolutionary structural concept, will welcome the re-cap with its new highlights and nuances.

'The Bailey Bridge is a prefabricated sectional bridge which is put together from interchangeable parts rather like a child's constructional toy and can be extended to almost any length or strengthened or added to as required. The bridge consists basically of a series of interchangeable lattice-work panels of electrically arc-welded special steel. These panels can be put end to end—as many as you like—and fastened together by steel pins inserted in holes. The pin is then locked by a split pin. Each panel can easily be lifted and carried by six men. Two lines of these connected panels, with steel beams laid across between them to carry the roadway, form the simple framework of the bridge. The roadway itself is built of wooden planks, all cut ready to standard size, and these are dropped into position and held down by a curb which is bolted down with hook bolts with captive nuts.

'The construction is simplicity itself. No "right" or "left hand" parts. No tools are required. Just a couple of standard spanners are needed—wheel brace spanners such as you use in bracing up the nuts of an automobile wheel. So there's no noise of hammering. The bridge can be erected under the cover of night. Building crews of about 40 men can handle these bridges after a week's training. In fact in emergency 40 raw recruits under one trained sergeant could make a good showing. They put the bridge together silently on the bank and then "launch" it. That is to say they move it forward on rollers; it has an extended nose, and as this nose touches the other side it bears the weight until the rest of the bridge has been rolled forward into position. It's a great advance on anything the Germans have produced. While the Nazis are fumbling with 25 nuts and bolts our men just push in a split pin.

'The Bailey Bridge is named after Donald Coleman Bailey, assistant superintendent at a Ministry of Supply Experimental Establishment who played a leading part in its design and development. General Montgomery has said "There is never enough Bailey bridging. This bridge is quite the best thing in that line we have ever had; it does everything we want." As an example of what it will do he mentioned that "even the 300 foot (90 metre) gap over the Trigno, with all the piers blown too, was bridged in 36 hours after the bridge ceased to be under aimed small arms fire."

'The bridge is simple, speedy, easy to construct. Parts of the bridge to take the heaviest tanks can be brought up in three-ton trucks. The heaviest part, the basic lattice-work panel, can be carried by six men — three a side. The roadway is wide enough to carry all military traffic. Additional traffic — two files of infantry on foot — can be carried at the same time by two footways. It is difficult to destroy the bridge structure completely by aerial bombardment. Some parts may be damaged by a direct hit or a near miss but thanks to the interchangeability of the parts, the damaged parts can be quickly replaced. Great care has to be taken in the factory in making the parts fit. The four corner holes of the panels are drilled out at one operation by four huge drills which have been mounted on a false baseplate, moved into the correct position, and then grouted in. Pins must fit easily into every hole and the fit must be perfect. To make absolutely sure that all parts will fit perfectly the panels are checked in the factory for interchangeability on specially made jigs. Time and trouble taken here ensure speed in erection in the field, so each panel is tested foursquare on a master jig and each pin must go in flush. Then, as a further test for interchangeability and at the same time for stress and strain, a 60 foot (18 metre) length of bridging panelling is actually put together in the factory and tested by a hydraulic ram which can apply any required load. Every single panel goes through this test too. This bridge of panels is constantly moving forward, panels being added at one end, as they are made, and taken off at the other end. Each panel gets its test of the full weight. This ingenious testing apparatus was specially invented for the purpose.'

One would think that these few examples of the veritable explosion of publicity in all the media both in Britain and world-wide would have ensured the name and fame of Donald Bailey in perpetuity, especially as he had been awarded the OBE and knighted in the interim. Yet in a matter of a year or so both he and his achievements were all but forgotten. It is true that the drama of a legal case he was compelled to instigate produced a slight flurry of interest but, basically a modest man, he sank without trace from the notice of the public. Only his colleagues and close friends knew he still existed.

In a revealing article in the *News Chronicle* of 23 January 1947, less than two years after the end of World War II, the writer of part two of a series entitled 'How are they now?' reported as follows: 'When I rang the Ministry of Supply and asked to speak to Sir Donald Bailey, the voice of authority answered "And who is Sir Donald Bailey?" Have you forgotten too? Don't you remember the Bailey bridges, the Sapper's dream, the perfect reply to the enemy's orgy of bridge destruction?'

His disappearance from public notice was not only compounded by his self-effacing reticence but also because he was engaged on foreign travel on assignments shrouded in confidentiality. I was so amazed that the story of Bailey and his bridge had never been told that in order to make certain I corresponded with Miss Jane With, an expert on the Book Information Service of the National Book League in London. She checked it out for me with courtesy and thoughtfulness and wrote to me: 'Again, I have not had much luck—anent the Bailey Bridge. The only title listed specifically on this in the copyright list is a technical handbook. There is no biography of Sir Donald Bailey, indeed his entry in *Who's Who* is so modest as not to mention his Bridge at all! I have telephoned the Institution of Structural Engineers—of which Sir Donald was a member, and their library has no title on the bridge, and no knowledge of any "standard" work!'

The thing which differentiates Donald Bailey's brainchild from, say, that of the Wright brothers is the fact that, while they invented a heavier than air machine of which we are constantly reminded as the majestic aeroplanes of today fly before our very eyes, Bailey only invented a bridge. As we know from previous chapters, history confirms there is nothing so taken for granted or so apt to be overlooked as that.

Donald Bailey, aged 40, in the plain khaki uniform of the Home Guard, in which he served for 4½ years. *Bailey Archives*.

Donald Bailey, in the foreground in his familiar sports jacket and cap, moves forward to inspect his bridge while it undergoes one of many tests at the Experimental Bridging Establishment, Christchurch, Hampshire, in 1941. *Bailey Archives.*

British light tanks cross an Inglis bridge. The bridge, like the tanks, was out of date in 1940. The top part was made of tubular steel components and a crisis came when the bridge buckled under a test load. *Imperial War Museum*.

A pyramid of tanks filled with scrap iron is used to test to breaking point a small section of Bailey bridging. This was the quickest and most convenient way of providing the necessary tonnage in the conditions of 1941. *Bailey Archives*.

Above: a thousand women in one vast area sit ready to correct Littlewoods football pool coupons in 1939.

Below: the same floor space in 1942 is turned over to the manufacture of Bailey Bridge pontoons. By the end of 1944 Littlewoods employed some 14,000 people in over 16 factories, making everything for the war effort, from parachutes to shells, from aircraft to barrage balloons. *Littlewoods*.

The contribution of women to the war effort in general and to Bailey Bridge manufacture in particular is shown by these two photographs. Above: a skilled operator at Littlewoods, Liverpool, uses an electric hand-saw. Below: girls assembling the frames of Bailey pontoons in jigs, work that required much concentration and precision. *Littlewoods*.

These two photographs show a team of Russian officers led by Major General Vasiliev examining a magnificent Bailey Bridge built over the wide River Sangro in central Italy by 10th Field Company of the Royal Canadian Engineers. *Imperial War Museum.*

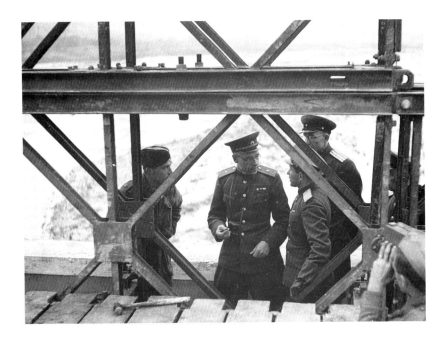

BAILEY BRIDGES DESIGNED AND MADE IN U.K.

Two war-time cartoons, the one above by Illingworth in the *Daily Mail* and below by Lee in the *London Evening News*, illustrate the popular appreciation of Donald Bailey and his Bridge. Official recognition was however harder to find. *Illingworth/Daily Mail/London Evening News/Harpur.*

"It's a nice little cottage, and if we can only get a Bailey Bridge from Army Surplus after the war . . ."

An artist's impression of sappers constructing a Bailey Bridge under fire.
Reproduced by kind permission of Littlewoods who commissioned the work.

'Make it good. Your son may have to use it' reads the notice over the assembly line at the International Steel Company plant at Evansville, Indiana. By 1945 nearly 4,000 sets of Bailey components, each capable of spanning 150 feet (46 metres) had been manufactured in the USA. *Bailey Archives.*

A smiling Winston Churchill in March 1945 walking across the impressive Bailey Bridge spanning the River Roer at Julich, one of the first German towns to fall into Allied hands. Field Marshal Montgomery is immediately behind him, together with Lieutenant General Simpson, the American general in whose sector the tour took place. *Imperial War Musuem.*

The Digger Bridge. This was a text-book example of a pontoon Bailey, leaping on floats across the Rhine at Xanten. It was nearly 1,200 feet (366 metres) long and was built by the 7th Army in March 1945. *Bailey Archives*.

The Bailey Bridge was a god-send in every theatre of war. This photograph shows a 440-foot (135-metre) suspension bridge built by American engineers over the Shweli River in Burma in 1945. *Bailey Archives*.

This historic photograph shows the first operational Bailey Bridge built on active service. Built on the night of 26 November, 1942, it spans the River Medjerda at Medjez el Bab in Tunisia, and was used by the newly formed Anglo-American First Army during their advance on Tunis in early 1943. *Imperial War Museum.*

General Eisenhower, Supreme Commander Allied Forces, visits a British sector in north-west Europe, walking over one of the many Bailey Bridges spanning the numerous canals. Twisted girders in the background are a grim reminder of German efficiency. *Imperial War Museum.*

This amazing Bailey in northern Italy shows the versatility of the bridge. Spanning a gap of 200 feet (60 metres), it runs to 390 feet (120 metres) and boasts a Bailey support tower of some 70 feet (20 metres) high. It was built by South Africans. *Imperial War Museum.*

Men of the 6th Royal Inniskillings smile for the camera as they cross a Bailey Bridge in Sicily, on their way to attack the enemy. This bridge was repeatedly hit by enemy fire and had to be erected five times before the Germans withdrew. *Imperial War Museum.*

These two photographs show clearly the problems which faced sappers clearing roads and bridge sites, with their noisy bulldozers, within range of enemy guns. Above: sappers and Indian troops working in the shadow of the 'Ubique' bridge near Rimini, Italy. Below: a bulldozer submerged in deep mud near the two Bailey Bridges used to cross the Rubicon. *Imperial War Museum.*

Dubbed 'The Impossible Bridge', this Bailey spanning the Moro in central Italy was built despite precipitous banks. Though only open for one-way traffic, it is more evidence for the sappers' ability to achieve the impossible in any conditions. *Imperial War Museum.*

Six steam traction engines being used to test the Callender-Hamilton bridge in 1937. They had to keep at 6-foot (about 2-metre) intervals while racing at their top speed, which was about 5 m.p.h. (8 km.p.h), without clutches or brakes. *Bailey Archives.*

Two examples of peacetime uses of Bailey bridging. These massive constructions were temporary expedients used in the building of hydroelectric and other schemes in Canada in the 1940s and early 1950s. Note the antlike size of the men in the bottom photograph. *Bailey Archives.*

Donald Bailey (left) enjoying a slice of a king-size melon. This photograph of a special party held in the snug bar of the King's Arms, Christchurch, typifies the more gregarious side of his character and the humour of his after-dinner speeches. *Bailey Archives.*

Sir Donald on his eightieth birthday is presented with a rose bowl by Major John Hathrell on behalf of his company, Thos. Storey. At left is Lady Bailey, his second wife, who masterminded the large cake with its perfect scale replica of a Bailey Bridge. *Bailey Archives.*

The Duke of Edinburgh visits Donald Bailey at Christchurch. According to Bailey himself, their descent into the boat was somewhat shaky and His Royal Highness joked as he straightened himself 'Who do you think I am – St. Peter?' *Bailey Archives*.

The so-called 'David and Goliath' bridges built over the River Seine at Vernon, France, in 1944. Goliath, in the foreground, was a massive Bailey, 694 feet (over 200 metres) long, which took heavy traffic. The David was built on nothing but folding boats. *Bailey Archives*.

Built in two months, the Freeman Bridge was one of the post-war semi-permanent bridges spanning the Rhine at Dusseldorf. It was a vital link when it was opened in October 1945, especially while the Wesel and Cologne bridges were being erected. *Bailey Archives.*

The floating Bailey Bridge built by Thos. Storey over the Demerara River in Guyana in the mid-1980s. This two-lane bridge runs to some 6,000 feet (about 2,000 metres). The gap is effected by retractable spans to allow ships to pass. *Thomas Storey (Engineering) Ltd.*

The versatility of the Bailey concept provided this launching tower and its supports for the successful 'Skylark' rocket tests in Australia in 1957. The structure was used many times. *British Aerospace.*

The precursor of the crane or fork-lift truck since time immemorial, an Indian elephant is used to construct an access Bailey Bridge on the Victoria Dam in Sri Lanka. *Thomas Storey (Engineering) Ltd.*

Alongside the Statue of Liberty, the 1,500-foot (450-metre) two-lane Bailey Bridge, built by Britain's Mabey and Johnson Ltd, is the vital link with the New York mainland for the 60-ton trucks of the contractors converting Ellis Island into part of the United States Heritage scheme. *Mabey and Johnson.*

8 The Saga of the Sappers

A good idea often evolves in three stages. First, someone has to have one. Secondly, someone has to recognize it when he or she sees it and give it finance and muscle to implement it. Thirdly, those given the finished product have to make it work. This last stage, in the case of Bailey's bridge could only be achieved by trying it out under active service conditions, especially in the heat of desperate battles. The bravery of the men who built the Bailey was of the same steel as that of the bridge itself. The sappers of the Allied armies never faltered under fire. It was as if they were inspired to reflect in their behaviour the highest standards and versatility which the bridge represented. They could not let down the bridge which would never let them down.

Donald Bailey stressed, as did those closest to him in those early days, that it was the dedicated effort, way beyond the call of duty, of a small team working flat out and enthusiastically together which brought the bridge project so speedily to successful completion. I was fortunate in meeting a few members of this team who could give first-hand accounts of the stupendous work they did. The advice and guidance given to me in particular by Sir Ralph Freeman, CVO, CBE (his father was the Chairman of the Structural Engineering Committee which helped Bailey so much) were invaluable. It was he who paved the way for my meeting Sir Donald Bailey who explained the mysteries of bridging to me with fascinating doodles. He also introduced me to Brigadier S.A. Stewart, CBE, and to Brigadier H.A.T. Jarrett-Kerr, CBE, who, as already mentioned, was a regular Royal Engineer design officer who made many of the final calculations and did a great deal of the detailed work at the EBE when much of the time Donald Bailey was away or working from his home.

But when the bridge went into action and was subjected to tests and pressures in combat conditions which even the genius of the EBE team could not anticipate, then those who were the very first to give it a baptism that would reveal its failure or success were the men of the Royal Engineers. Their experience would determine whether or not it fulfilled all expectations and if it could be adopted by the Allied armies.

To set the scenario of the tasks undertaken by the Royal Engineers I will borrow a few paragraphs from my book *The Impossible Victory* published by Wm. Kimber in 1980. My main reason for so doing is because I was rewarded by scores of letters from sappers and from other front-line soldiers thanking me for describing it 'as it was'. Three paragraphs encapsulate a broad description of those bloody battles.

'The Germans built strong defensive lines on the high ground overlooking each river. They were very good at it and as they withdrew they got better and better. The American Fifth Army advancing up the west coast of Italy, and the British Eighth Army moving along the Adriatic side, found the same heartbreak and horror every few miles as they in turn attempted each crossing and tried to dislodge the well-prepared enemy.

'The same pattern of this warfare of attrition was to be repeated over and over again. Invariably the bridges were blown up, and the first job was to ferry patrols across under cover of darkness to probe the enemy positions, to search for minefields, and to establish a bridgehead if possible so that the sappers could push a Bailey bridge over the gap in the one that had been blown, or at some convenient point nearby on pontoons. All this had to be done by troops who were already exhausted, who had to work in terrain which was familiar exclusively to the enemy, in pitch black darkness, and as often as not in pouring rain. In addition enemy fighting patrols, counter-attacks, and well directed fire from mobile guns and mortars, all aimed at the spots which he knew well in advance were the most likely crossing places, caused mayhem. It was a recurrent nightmare.

'The wider the water, the greater were the odds in favour of the defence, and the Germans prepared many months in advance to fortify the major rivers accordingly. They had recruited large work forces from the Todt organization and local population for this purpose. Observation posts, gun emplacements, vast minefields, machine-gun nests galore, food, fuel, and ammunition dumps were all skilfully sited, protected, and camou-flaged. In addition a host of minor ploys calculated to cause disruption and death ranging from trip wires and booby traps to individual snipers were used extensively. But the gallant sappers would not be stopped. They built their Bailey come what may.'

Donald Bailey handed me the typescript of a talk he gave towards the end of the war, in which he emphasized the heroic role of the sappers. He said: 'I would like to say a little bit about the work which the Royal Engineers have put in in erecting these bridges all over the world. It is not merely a question of erecting standard bridges over nicely prepared sites — as so often occurs in training. The site is probably on or near the place where an existing bridge has been demolished and cluttered up with tons of rubble, twisted steelwork, and other wreckage. It may very well be under fire by the enemy and, in all probability, no detailed reconnaissance will have been possible. The first task which faces the sappers is to clear away a large number of mines which will undoubtedly have been broadcast all over the site. Then must come the bulldozers to clear away the rubbish in order to give them room to work at all. It may be necessary to put down smoke screens to hide from the enemy what is going on, and to give the harassed men a chance to avoid being picked off by small-arms fire. The lorries carrying the equipment must be brought up and unloaded close to the site, during which time the gap must be measured and arrangements made to strengthen foundations, if necessary. So much preparatory work has to be done before the first panel is put in place and ticking away all the time are the minutes leading up to the completion deadline.'

I culled from the *Royal Engineers Journal* a story provided by Derrick Vernon, a platoon commander of 24th Field Company, Royal Engineers, which brings one face to face, indeed eyeball to eyeball, with the realities of bridging operations in battle in the most simple and laconic fashion. Heroism without heroics is expressed in the most understated language. His Company comprised some 240 sappers with 50 vehicles. They arrived in Normandy in July 1944. After spending some time on a variety of mundane jobs, the main one being that of essential road maintenance, for as one knows sappers are expected to do a thousand dull as well as dangerous jobs, they moved forward. By the end of September they eventually came to a small village in Holland.

The canal bridge just beyond the village had been destroyed and the far bank of the canal was in enemy hands. A joint Anglo-American operation was planned to assault the canal and rebuild the bridge. The sappers waited just out of range of the sporadic shellfire while a brother officer, one Lieutenant Bob Harris, carried out a stealthy night reconnaissance. He and his driver were lucky. Approaching the destroyed bridge their armoured car was blown up on a mine but miraculously both escaped unharmed. Shaken, but with a singleness of purpose which their vital task imposed, they pressed on with the task. After careful testing they concluded that the water was too deep for the assaulting infantry to cross without risk of drownings. Worse still, they found that the ground was too soft to get tanks over on a new bridge which would need to be 60 feet (18 metres) long and strong enough to take a 40-ton load. So, what to do? There was only one answer.

It was decided to build a footbridge, initially to enable the infantry to dash across and seize the other bank. Perhaps not so much a 'dash' as a tense little trot following blindly the man in front. This required speedy

61

organization and one platoon put the footbridges together and moved them forward. The other platoons waited in their transport in the village. There was a lot of spasmodic shelling but no casualties. They waited patiently for the promised artillery barrage to support the attack across the footbridge, but something went wrong with the fire plan. Then followed nothing except a disappointing silence. The platoon with the footbridges were on their way crawling and heaving the half-ton loads along the deep ditches. The American infantrymen were with them. They all got very wet and dirty but being in good cover were relatively safe. There was heavy machine-gun fire and reports of snipers. More infantrymen moved up in half-track vehicles. Some ambulance jeeps returned with wounded men. A continual dull thump of shells and mortars exploded in the soft sodden ground and now it poured with rain. The platoons in the village waited in vain for news of their mates up front. There was an agonizing silence. They had strict orders not to move until the bridgehead was secure—which would take time. No natural cover lay beyond the canal bank; men would be very exposed and would have to advance carefully. To add to the problems and congestion, the heavy bridging company lorries moved up closer, in the hope that the attack would succeed. Darkness fell. The rain continued unabated. The lowering skies promised a bad night ahead.

But then, glory be, the footbridge platoon came stumbling back smothered in mud and oozing water from their battledress. It was unbelievable but somehow they had floated their footbridges over the canal enabling 250 infantrymen to cross dry shod. Emerging from the ditches they had achieved considerable surprise, but had been pinned to the ground by heavy shelling and a barrage of six-barrel mortars—the 'moaning minnies' as they were dubbed. Amazingly the platoon suffered only one casualty, a fortunate outcome which shows that sometimes those who dare can win. It is not surprising that the platoon gained three awards for bravery in this particular action.

Derrick Vernon and his colleagues were as assured as they could be that the bridgehead was secure but for some reason or another they felt considerable unease. The proper bridge had to be completed by first light the following morning, but they had already lost a valuable hour or more of darkness. There were only 11 hours to complete the action if they were not to be exposed as sitting ducks at dawn. They led the bridging column in their radio-equipped armoured cars, moving quietly up the pitch-black road littered with fallen trees and damaged vehicles, and keeping well away from the verges which they thought were mined. They were guided only by the stark outline of some bordering trees to within a short distance from the canal.

Their heavy tools and equipment were unloaded silently, and there began an immediate and systematic search for mines and booby traps around the demolished bridge site and the grass verges nearby. The wooden 'Schu' mines laid in vast numbers by the Germans could not be found by mine detectors as they contained no metal, and so could only be located by careful prodding of the ground. The 'Schu' mine was not very powerful but its charge was sufficient to blow a limb off or an even more important part of the soldier's anatomy. So, in the dark and wet, they slung stout hanks of rope between their legs from the front to the back of their trousers, hoping that, if any of them was unlucky enough to lose a foot or both feet or a leg, at least he would still be eligible for other pursuits, as they delicately put it. Fortunately the demolition of the bridge had left the abutments intact but large pieces of reinforced concrete had to be removed from the road-surface before bridging could begin. There being no adequate turning area available, the six-wheeled bridging lorries were reversed at little more than a snail's pace, a mile to the canal. One can imagine what slow torture this must have been. They had to avoid touching the verges as one mined lorry would have wrecked the whole operation by blocking the narrow road. They could only be unloaded one at a time.

The equipment had to be stacked on this same narrow road with some of it at an inconvenient distance to keep the road clear and to preserve movement. The low reverse gears made an unbelievable noise in the silence of the night; the clanging of steel on steel as the lorries were unloaded could not fail to be heard, yet with an instinct for preservation the men were talking in whispers! They were now well above the level of the surrounding ground which was mostly peat and felt very exposed. Mortar bombs and shells shrieked at intervals into the soft turf around them but so long as they landed there and not on the tarmac road they were fairly safe. The darkness was intense. They had great difficulty in finding all the parts needed and the use of any lights was out of the question. In building the Bailey most of the parts are wanted at the same time and they had to hurry. They were only protected by the darkness of the night. Holes had to be felt for, small bits found, the site was wet and increasingly slippery, muttered oaths and curses rent the air as fingers were trapped, some items were difficult to fit. Furthermore it was hard to keep the construction straight as the levelling had been hurried. There was the constant fear of mines underfoot and of mortar bombs and shells landing among them. The occasional star shell illuminated the sky. Progress was agonizingly slow. In the most frustrating moments an NCO's muted voice could be heard exhorting his comrades to keep trying. The night continued to be shattered by salvoes of mortar bombs, six at a time. Shells they did not hear exploded in the peat, but scattered small-arms fire, seemingly from nowhere, singed the air around them.

Burning buildings to the north and artificial moonlight created by searchlights covering the Division's attack, served only to intensify the blackness. Derrick Vernon was not contacted by the Americans shielding the bridgehead, and several times he crouched and crept along the deserted road ahead into no-man's land, attempting to find out just where they might be. This task was fraught with the risk of being shot, but they were not to be found. So the sappers depleted their working strength to post men to protect those building the bridge.

Vernon and his NCOs continued to cajole and inspire their men to work against the clock, knowing full well that if the bridge was not finished by first light—and the October dawn would break quickly—they would certainly suffer heavy casualties. There could be no question of retreating before the job was done. Unless the bridge was completed, reinforcements could not reach those hanging on desperately on the other side, and the battle would be lost. It was just like Termoli all over again.

Time passed. The voices of the trusty Sergeants Ron Brewer and Bob Cushen became more impatient and demanding—they had no wish to be caught in the open at daybreak. But for all the strenuous effort, they had problems. Some of the jacks for lowering the bridge on to its base did not function properly and worse still the dawn came with some bits of the bridge incomplete. When the light exposed them the mortar bombs started to arrive with growing accuracy.

Lance Sergeant Baker took a small party to windward to cover the site with smoke using smoke-pots designed for this purpose. It was so effective that soon the sappers were all choking! Then came several bursts of machine-gun fire nearby. Time was running out. Soon ominous black puffs in the sky approaching steadily overhead warned them that they were about to be strafed with air-bursting shells. In a frenzied finale before disaster struck, the bridge was completed. It just sufficed to take the first tanks of the 11th Armoured Division. The sappers' task was done. They were completely exposed in the broadening daylight. It was pointless to risk so many lives by waiting to put up a few finishing touches to the bridge. They decided to retire. But their problems were far from over.

Once again Murphy's dictum was confirmed that if anything can go wrong, it will. Vernon and his driver, praying for a fast getaway, found that their scout car would not start. It was prone to blockage of the petrol filter. They did not propose to leave it behind, so Vernon raised the engine cover and unscrewed the filter coated with sediment. His driver pressed the starter, a stream of clean petrol washed the filter clean. The filter was replaced in record time and off they went.

I will leave the rest of this episode to be described in Derrick Vernon's own words. Their pithy and poignant simplicity says it all.

'A mile down the road we ordered a hurried roll-call, one of my section Lance Corporals was missing, Jackson, a quiet man from a Durham mining village. "Jacko" was last seen by the smoke pots. I decided to search for him and scrambled back to the bridge under the protection of the deep drainage ditch. The smoke had long since given out. I searched the desolate expanse of peat and heather. I shouted his name but there was no reply. The mortars were firing again. I was convinced they were firing at me! Reluctantly I concluded Jackson was missing and if I stayed much longer, I would be too. As I withdrew, a troop of three Sherman tanks which had come up close to the bridge attracted again a ferocious barrage of shelling and "moaning minnies". I sought cover, and laid underneath a tank whilst the air shrieked with sound and the ground shook. I shook too and prayed the tank, whose crew were unaware of my presence, would not decide to move. There was a lull and I rejoined my men, dismayed to be told that Jackson was not to be found.

'Very soon afterwards the tanks and supporting infantrymen of the leading Brigade crossed the bridge, "Jacko's Bridge" as it was later named, followed closely by a section of Number 1 Platoon under the indomitable Bob Walters to fix the decking. They too were pinned down by a vicious barrage and sought shelter under the girders. The steel work was later found to be cut through in many places (the bridge was later rebuilt) and the attacking infantry suffered many casualties. As the attack pressed forward, the firing ceased. Bob Walters found "Jacko" lying in the heather near the smoke pots. He had been hit many times and would have died instantly. Only 40 yards (36 metres) away the unseen Spandau machine gun we had heard during the final stages of construction was found abandoned. I shall never know why the machine gunner did not turn his gun on the crowded bridging party but perhaps we were hidden very effectively in the smoke. Amongst the fallen British infantry struck down as they crossed the foot bridges and the main bridge, on the canal bank near the smoke pots that had protected us all in the dangerous half hour after dawn—we buried Jacko where he fell; the Officer's Field Service Pocket Book had many uses and thoughtfully includes a form of service for such occasions.'

I am again indebted to Derrick Vernon for his classic account of the historic crossing of the Rhine. As he said himself 'as a young officer, however, one did not see the grand strategy, only the men one knew and lost, one saw the frail equipment and its problems, the wide treacherous river and the far bank'.

After a brief spot of leave he rejoined his Company to learn of plans being made to cross the gigantic river in assault boats and in the teeth of fierce enemy resistance. On 23 March 1945 the final decisions were made. At 3 a.m. the following morning, when one hastens to emphasize that man is not often at his best, he took a small party to the edge of the river where an armoured bulldozer was at work and just before completing the job the driver was shot through the chest. On Vernon's left another company of Royal Engineers had managed to get across the Rhine in assault boats and they were busy trying to establish a bridgehead against the enemy lying low in their slit trenches and well hidden in the darkness. He returned to his farmhouse shelter at dawn and as he was marshalling his equipment he was caught in the open by a sharp attack of shelling. The farm was obviously a certain target for enemy guns and within a few seconds several men were killed and wounded. One of the sappers, a young man of only 19 years, had the great misfortune to be killed by a splinter which, by cruel fate, entered the narrow visor of Vernon's armoured car. He himself was dazed by a splinter furrowing his steel helmet. Others had similar narrow escapes. This was a bad start, but as the shelling died down he heard from radio control that two platoons on rafting operations, already on the water's edge as daylight broke, were under heavy mortar and small-arms fire.

Work had temporarily ceased and they were furiously digging in to protect themselves from unnecessary losses. The infantry had unfortunately missed the Spandau machine-gun nests opposite them. These were eventually knocked out by direct hits from the armoured cars, but not before the first two rafts built had been sunk by machine-gun fire. About three hours later the far bank was cleared and Vernon's platoon was able to get on with building their rafts on top of pontoons which were powered by outward engines. With these they ran a regular ferry service backwards and forwards to bring in reinforcements which would have done credit to the most efficient cross-channel operators.

When, overburdened by fatigue, they were ordered to stop, it was calculated that his band of sappers had made about 700 round trips in 72 hours across a very dangerous river in flimsy craft. Nine were killed in the action and 20 were wounded.

I am indebted to Colonel J.H. Frankeau MC for reminding us that, although statistics about bridges are abundant and of great fascination to engineers, it was a fact that the gallant sappers spent much more time on other vital matters like clearing mines, constructing mule and jeep tracks, tank tracks, tank fords, roads, quarries, and air strips. The latter permitted the take-off and landing of the light aircraft used for aerial reconnaissance and as flying observation posts for our artillery. They added to their repertoire the digging of culverts, producing water points, filling in large craters, and revetting high embankments to prevent minor or even major landslides caused by torrential rain. In the rear areas and often within shell shot they performed miracles in repairing and maintaining railway lines and services. There was nothing they could not or would not do. Like London's famous Windmill Theatre, the sappers in World War II never closed. While others slept they worked 24 hours a day for every day of the year's 365.

Colonel R.M. Foster, DSO, OBE, leavens the arduous mix of the sapper's experience with a dramatic and somewhat amusing anecdote following the capture of Le Havre in September 1944. It appeared that a group of sappers in two half-track vehicles went forward at night to do the nasty job of neutralizing booby traps but in the dark they missed our forward troops and, horror of horrors, bumped into a German patrol on the road in no-man's-land. Their mutual exchange of fire caused 'impartial' but concentrated mortar fire from both sides. Everyone took to the road-side ditches. Two sappers found a German between them in their ditch and informed him that he was surrounded and a prisoner. He was nothing loth and in good English stated that he intended to desert anyway and would be pleased to guide his captors back to their lines as they had obviously lost their way.

Another bridging epic was that of the crossing of the River Rapido which was a precursor of the final bitter battle for the town and Monastery of Cassino in central Italy. Lieutenant Colonel A.P. de T. Daniell MC, TD, RE, set off to reconnoitre the proposed site for his Bailey bridge on the evening of 27 April 1944. He was accompanied by his officers Boston and Chubb and Sergeant Cox. All four carried tommy-guns.

They had arranged to rendezvous at one of the Company HQs of the Indian Battalion who were then holding the river. They were given the password and they told the Indians where they were going and that they hoped to be back in about an hour. The river was in no-man's-land, and was freely patrolled by both British and Germans alike.

They went down an approach track to the river. It was rather light with a half moon, very quiet, and extremely eerie. The river had a flood bank of shingle which had at some time been dredged out of it. There was still plenty of American equipment lying about and some very unpleasant smells. However they made their way slowly, keeping below the bank, and stopping often to listen. Having reached the bend in the river they were aiming for, Sergeant Cox lay on the bank with his tommy-gun cocked as lookout man. Meanwhile the other three had a long argument as to who should swim the river in order to measure its width. Boston wanted to swim but the Colonel thought there was too much moonlight and was against it. At this moment Cox rolled down the bank to whisper the startling news that there were four enemy on the other side. So they all peered cautiously over the bank and there they were, four of them, quite clear, only about 80 feet (24 metres) away. They must have been sappers too, for each carried a shovel on his shoulder. What an easy target! The Colonel was itching to pull the trigger, but decided against it as he did not want to give the game away.

However, that finally decided the issue. No one would swim that night. They quietly measured up the area for space to dump stores and build the bridge. The shingle bank was about four feet (1.2 metres) high, so they decided it would have to be bulldozed through. There was also an annoying little dry ditch plumb in the middle of the building area. They took all the measurements and decided to clear out back to the road without more ado. Having reached the road, they checked in with the Indians with considerable relief and drove home. They immediately got down to prepare the outline plan. Sappers never have time to spare. Every minute spent on thorough preparation could make all the difference. For

67

the want of a minute of forethought, like the want of the proverbial nail, the battle could be lost.

The next morning the Colonel took his plan to his Chief. The only real comment arising from it was, of course, the fact that someone simply had to get across the river to measure its width accurately and to see what the far bank was like. The big question promptly arose as to who should swim across, an officer or another volunteer who was a good swimmer? On the logical basis of there being only one officer to 68 men it was decided not to risk an officer and so volunteers were called for. There were plenty—morale in the company was very high just then. Anything for a bit of excitement. Driver McTighe was chosen. He was the best swimmer in the company and Boston's own driver. It was decided to try again the following night, but when the time came there was too much light with a very bright moon. So the attempt was put off for a day. Luckily next night, 30 April, was cloudy and just right. It was their last chance before the battle started.

This time the same party with the addition of Driver McTighe gathered together. Again they set off by jeep at dusk and again they called on the Indians and warned them of their movements. This was even more necessary as these Indians were now extremely light on the trigger and delighted in shooting at strangers. They arrived at their bend in the river and all was quiet.

The Colonel lay on the bank to the left with tommy-gun cocked and watched the enemy bank intently. So did Sergeant Cox some 40 yards (36 metres) to the right. Boston and McTighe in the centre prepared to measure the water gap. McTighe took off his clothes but wore canvas shoes, dark bathing pants, and a brown pullover borrowed from the Colonel to hide the white of his body. Doubtless it also helped to mitigate the freezing impact of the icy water. He tied the end of the measuring tape to his stomach, waded in, and swam quickly across, being carried a few yards downstream. He was just making his way upstream under the far bank to get opposite to Boston when two loud explosions went off over his head. He gave a tug on the tape which was the signal for Boston at the water's edge to pull tight the scrap of white tape through which the measuring line had run. Either McTighe had set off a trip wire or the enemy had heard him and had lobbed over a couple of speculative grenades. At all events he was untouched and swam the 60-odd feet (about 20 metres) back twice as fast as he had ever swum in his life. Once they were both over on the friendly side they bundled up their belongings and beat a hasty retreat. They were naturally afraid that if they delayed, the enemy might bring down a concentration of mortar fire on the bank. However, all was well.

Back on the road McTighe put on his clothes and they inspected the tape. It measured only 52 feet (16 metres). This seemed a little short but nobody fancied doing it again. So they drove home to ponder on the plan. Colonel Daniell went off the very next day to discuss the situation with his Chief. The figure of 52 feet was questioned as being unreliable but calculations from aerial photographs confirmed its accuracy. A figure of 55 feet (17 metres) was accepted as the width of the water and in fact when the bridge came to be built this was found to be correct.

Having withdrawn for several days to rehearse their role over and over again, the scene was set at last for the assault across the aptly named fast-flowing River Rapido. Our sappers came forward once more and the Colonel, who was sitting on the ground with some 25 of his men around him, got an immediate taste of the terror to come. Suddenly shells started arriving. They came roaring in all over the place. All they could do was to lie flat, pressed to the earth, and pray to the Lord, while the ground shook and heaved all round. It was terrifying. The Colonel literally bit the dust trying to make himself smaller. In two minutes it was all over. They were on the receiving end of 80 shells — 10 rounds of gunfire from two batteries. And the incredible thing was that not a soul was hurt, except one unfortunate Sapper Hughes who was sitting on the latrine and stopped a small fragment of shrapnel. A great deal of their kit, motor-cycles, and the few trucks they had with them were drilled with more holes than a colander. No whit dismayed they took all this as a good omen avowing that their luck must be in.

The big attack started at 10 p.m. on 12 May. Suddenly the heavens were rent open and every gun fired simultaneously. There were about 900 guns in the barrage. The noise was indescribable. The flashes made it as light as day, but infinitely more lurid. Nearer the river itself the continuous swish of shells could be heard passing overhead. Against the backcloth of battle bombardment, with the flash and thunder of rearing guns splitting the heavens, the sapper waiting tensely to start on his bridge felt a numb humility. It seemed his only option was to do or die.

Meanwhile there was a sinister development on the other side of the water. The Germans did not retreat under the barrage, but instead came forward to line the shingle bank of the river with machine-guns. And, not only was it a still night with a natural mist hanging over the river, but to add to the general confusion, the enemy thickened up this natural mist with dense smoke till it was an impenetrable fog some 100 yards (90 metres) or more in depth. Into this blanket of pea soup fog the infantry advanced on a wide front carrying their boats in good order straight towards the river. But once in the fog they were lost. Some went right, some went left, and nearly all went round in circles, coming back out of the fog into unfamiliar surroundings. Meanwhile the enemy, with visibility down to zero, fired his Spandau machine-guns blindly at random into the fog as well as mortaring spasmodically all along the river. All this fire was, of course, unobserved and therefore not all that dangerous, but in the fog it was extremely frightening. A few of the boats did get across. But their main intention on landing was to get away from the river and seize their objectives inland. This they did, but in moving forward they neglected to clear the enemy off the far bank. There was nobody available to follow up to perform this vital and bloody task. Having only sufficient men to cope with their engineer's role, the sappers could not be committed to making the assault as infantry-men. Things, as always, were not going according to plan.

Colonel Daniell set up his Bridge HQ at the top of the approach track and at the same time their old bulldozer trundled down it. This seemed to enrage the enemy who concentrated all his available fire in the direction of the sound.

This brought the bulldozer to a standstill, wounding one driver, but not until he had got almost to the bank. Thereafter every time he started up a hail of bullets came over. Next other sappers arrived with the first of the lorries carrying the bridge equipment. But nothing could be done in that awful fog with bullets whizzing overhead. The only solution was to get some infantry across to deal with the Spandaus. But where to find the men who could do it?

Colonel Daniell, who was now joined by his Chief, set out to search for any officers or warrant officers who could help, but not one could be found. Dejected parties of infantry were still milling around with their boats. Meanwhile, however, Boston had swum across with a rope and secured both ends to trees and passing it through the bow loop of an assault boat, he made a foolproof ferry. He then found an infantry officer who raised a platoon and promised to clear out the Germans. But they soon came back, having got hopelessly lost in the fog. The Spandaus kept up their burst which sounded like the sudden ripping of corrugated paper.

All this time, of course, the bridging lorries had been arriving strictly according to timetable and were merely piling up at the top of the track. They were stopped eventually, but not until at least 20 out of the 32 had arrived. During this time Chubb was able to do a bit of improvement on the track, but even that was hideously difficult and several track-material lorries were hit.

As the night wore on, this state of chaos increased steadily and to cut a long exasperating story short, when dawn began to break, absolutely nothing had been achieved. More disasters followed. The enemy must have seen or sensed the concentration of vehicles at the top of the track, for suddenly he began shelling. Then followed half an hour of hell, while they tried to turn the trucks round and get them out of it. One officer, Lieutenant Williams, did magnificent work, before finally being seriously wounded. Sergeant Cox was also badly wounded in this jam of struggling vehicles. At the same time the Colonel's scout car, which was his Bridge HQ carrying his wireless links, received a bit of shrapnel the size of a fist through the radiator, much to the consternation of Company Sergeant Major Tutton inside.

Things now looked desperate. It was full daylight and the Germans were putting over 'Minenwerfers' in salvoes of six. The river was clearly in view from the Monastery and so were they. Retreat was inevitable and the word was passed round to all the men to return individually to their old field at the rear. The Colonel and his officers, Boston and Chubb, walked slowly back together. Their heads were down. Their tails were down. Not a word was spoken. What was there to say?

However, despite numerous mishaps, casualties, confusion, and the eternal fog of war, both metaphorical and real in this case, the sappers came back, and back again, to build that vital bridge. Gradually it took shape.

For some time one particular Spandau had been causing almost continuous interference and quite a few casualties. So Sergeant Parry of 59th Field Company decided to go across on the launching nose and deal with this man. He lay full-length on the leading crossbeam until it grounded and at once ran a few yards along the bank, throwing himself on the ground to take cover. When the Spandau opened fire he got the direction and made a dash towards the spot, firing two magazines of his tommygun. The Spandau did not fire again. Sergeant Parry returned to organize getting the launching nose on to rollers. When the job of lifting the nose on to rollers was done and the bridge moved forward again, more Spandau bursts appeared to be coming from directly inland. Again Sergeant Parry, this time with Sapper Halliday, decided to go after it. They were going straight towards its direction when they heard cries to the right. On going to investigate they found two wounded men, an officer with his foot blown off by a Schu mine and a badly wounded sergeant. Sergeant Parry took the officer back to the bridge on his back, while Sapper Halliday and Sapper Coombs carried the sergeant back. Sergeant Parry and Sapper Halliday, not content with their heroic feat, then returned to shoot up the Spandau. They located it because its line of fire gave its position away. They closed in on it with tommy-guns blazing and put it and its crew out of action.

The bridge was now almost complete an hour before dawn broke. Every available man, plus the bulldozer, stood round to push it into position. This required a strong heave as it was an up-hill launch. All went well until with 20 feet (6 metres) to go, the bulldozer gave out completely, having seized up. Both radiator and sump had been punctured some time before.

This was a major disaster, as the bridge could not be moved by hand alone. However they suddenly remembered the tanks. Boston went to get the leading tank and the Colonel went to the wireless set to report the delay, and the action which was being taken. When he got back to the site he was delighted to see that the tank had pulled the bulldozer out of the way and was slowly pushing the bridge forward. The enemy took extreme exception to this and put down a number of well-aimed mortar rounds causing several casualties. It was therefore decided not to bother about jacking down, but to push the bridge clean off the rollers on to the ground. It did in fact fall nicely on the base plates. But the far side still had to be jacked up to remove the rollers. Once this was done the launching nose was dismantled and the ramps were quickly built. Soon afterwards the tanks crossed with support vehicles. The bridgeheads were bolstered with more troops, ammunition, and rations. The breakthrough in the bloody battle of Cassino had come at last.

We must not lose sight of the essential fact that, but for Mr Bailey and his exceedingly ingenious bridge, the courageous dedication of the sappers would almost certainly have been frustrated in providing the link which enables the front-line infantry to get their tanks and reinforcements in time. Previous attempts to cross the River Rapido and many other rivers were utter failures involving great losses of lives and equipment when that vital piece of military Meccano was not at hand or unable through enemy action to be deployed.

Indeed so decisive was the effect of the Bailey Bridge on the course of the campaign that the Germans in their retreat eventually concentrated their mining to catch the sappers and their bulldozers rather than the infantry and tanks, because the progress of the Allied advance was dependent upon the speed of engineering work. Not only was the debris of blown bridges mined as a matter of course, but any obvious diversion around the blown bridge was more heavily mined. There would be anti-tank mines and anti-personnel mines near the surface and also a few deep mines dropped down specially drilled holes which would blow up a bulldozer when it had been working on site for some time. Furthermore many mines were now unresponsive to detectors, so reliance could be placed only on slow, careful, and frequent prodding by hand.

An example of the priority the Germans gave to the destruction of the Bailey was recounted by Colonel R. N. Foster. An attempt to do a night bridging operation across a river in Holland was interrupted by enemy shelling every single time the sappers made a move. This extraordinary coincidence was explained when, in the morning, three Germans were discovered hidden in the abutments of the old bridge with a wireless set. This they had used to direct the fire from their own artillery each time they heard work starting on the site. They knew that if they did not stop the Bailey there was nothing left but to retreat.

One of the things which pleased Donald Bailey immensely was the assurance given to him that the soldiers who had to build his bridge genuinely took to it. He said more than once with brevity and sincerity 'I'm glad the soldiers like my bridge'. Just to bear this out I have chosen extracts from two letters which in their different ways illustrate the virtual infallibility of the bridge and ease of handling. No wonder the soldiers liked it.

Sergeant Penfold of Dorset said: 'The nose of the bridge always seemed to reach a point where it would topple before reaching the other side, and fall into the drink. Yet it never failed to arrive safely thanks to the counterbalance. While my Company did not assemble the bridge we dismantled them to be sent forward again for further use. How extraordinarily easy it all seemed. The simplicity of the bridge and its handling equipment commanded our respect and satisfaction in working on it.'

Mr Harry Stembridge of Leicester sent me a potted history of his 106th Bridge Company of the Royal Army Service Corps which was attached to sapper units to transport Bailey bridge equipment. In it are listed more than 60 place-names where after D-Day the bridging operations were carried out. There was only one failure reported and that was due not to a defect in equipment but to continuous bombardment by heavy enemy guns.

Finally in tribute to the sappers, as gallant and remarkable a breed of men as one could meet, I will draw on an account by Mr R. J. P. Cowan, a former RE officer, which demonstrates vividly that sappers could build bridges in human and public relation terms with the same panache and ease of handling as they built their Bailey. Mr Cowan was one of the advance party destined to build a port on the Normandy coast when the invasion started. He writes: 'Early on D-Day, 6 June 1944, Colonel Raymond Mais, with Major Bobby Court, CSM George Braysford, and a small advance party, waded ashore through the surf at Le Hamel, found their way along the narrow Normandy lanes through scattered units of a very hostile German Army, to the little seaside village of Arromanches, where the port was to be built. There he met Brigadier Walter, who arrived in some style with his batman in a large power boat which he had somehow "acquired" during the darkness off shore from our American Allies. Both men were lucky to have escaped death that morning.

'The main body of the Company caught up with them during the early hours of the following day. It was hot. Confused fighting was going on all around the village. German tanks had been seen nosing out of the woods less than half a mile away and there was that never-to-be-forgotten feeling in the air of crackling tension that one gets when sudden, violent death is about.

'Two officers, namely Brigadier Walter and Raymond Mais, had just started to explain the first tasks to be done when, round the corner on the sea front, came an old Frenchman with his wife and daughter. It was obvious that they were frightened to death. The women were weeping and only pride was keeping the old man going. They stopped short, extremely frightened, when they saw the British sappers, wondering for a moment if they were friend or foe. Brigadier Walter and Raymond Mais put down their map cases. "Wally" Walter walked over to the ladies while Raymond Mais gave the old man a crashing salute. He was heard, in absolutely appalling French, trying to congratulate the old fellow on bringing his ladies to safety through the enemy lines, and to express the hope that they would accept the hospitality of the British Royal Engineers. Meanwhile "Wally" Walter was chatting up and charming the two ladies. He had found chairs for them, and had jollied them into laughing and talking and attending to their appearance. The old Frenchman, his pride and his dignity restored, then joined them. This spontaneous expression of the entente cordiale was brought to a happy conclusion when they were given hot tea, food, and shelter by the Company Sergeant Major.

'This act of kindness, indeed of chivalry, by these two officers, did not pass unnoticed by the sappers. It fortified the mutual respect and affection which the officers and the other ranks had for each other.

'The same evening, at dusk, they camped in an orchard just outside the village. It was noisier than ever. A battle had developed on the hillside only a few hundred yards away with machine-gun fire, mortar bombs, tracer bullets, flares, and shells criss-crossing in an inferno of confusion. The perimeter of the orchard was manned and they settled down, uneasily, for the night.

'Suddenly, as sometimes happens, a hush fell over the battlefield. Only the silent flares, slowly descending, remained. By their light the sappers were astonished to see Colonel Mais slipping into the most fashionable pale blue silk pyjamas with a floral motif embroidered on the front of primroses and forget-me-nots—obviously the work of some loved one. They never found out if the gallant Colonel habitually wore pale blue silk pyjamas on the battlefield, but the very sight of them turned their thoughts to more gentle and happier things. So they settled down for the night, in that dark Normandy wood, forgetting for a moment the dangers around them. It is recorded that the Colonel's somewhat unusual night attire for the battlefield did wonders for morale and "steadied the raw and nervous troops."

'This also illustrates one of the great strengths of the British Army— not exactly taught at the Royal Military Academy at Sandhurst but enshrined there on passing out day for the fledgling Officers when the Adjutant rides his horse up the steps to enter the main building, while still mounted.'

An Officer blessed with a little eccentricity is a perpetual source of wonder and even affection with the ordinary soldier. Every regiment and corps can boast one or more of these idiosyncratic idols entrusted with the Monarch's commission. This has led to the story, apocryphal or true, it does not matter, of the Officer steeped in such strange behaviour that the troops would follow him anywhere—even out of curiosity!

Ex-sapper Mr Howard Deeming provided an amusing variation on the theme of the bridge's versatility. It appears that during the advance through Belgium a Bailey Bridge had been built over one of the canals. After the advance from this spot a Field Company of the Royal Engineers went to recover the bridge for future use. On arrival they were confronted by a very irate elderly Belgian who tried to prevent them from removing the bridge. Apparently the man had been running a ferry service there before the bridge existed. However some of our enterprising soldiers with an eye to business sold him the bridge. So instead of rowing people across the canal he charged them for crossing it. Of course when the recovery squad came to dismantle it, he was really upset at the thought of a regular source of income being whisked away.

Perhaps the crowning story came from an old soldier writing from Leicester: 'In 1945 I was in the first lot to cross the River Po as an amphibious tank driver but we returned to the south bank for some reason I now forget. But on our return north we crossed the Bailey bridge which was said to be the second largest built. The funny bit was that the sappers had taken a chamber pot from a nearby house, a bright yellow one, filled it with flowers and put a notice under it saying "This is the Po but don't stop to piss in it".'

I am indebted to Mr. Hanton of Southampton for sending me a picture of the triumphant and proud notice at the entrance to probably one of the longest Bailey Bridges ever built. It spanned the width of the Rhine. It was named MONTGOMERY BRIDGE and the text explained:

'THIS BRIDGE IS 2032 FEET LONG, 2400 TONS OF BAILEY BRIDGE AND 6720 TONS OF REINFORCED CONCRETE WERE USED IN ITS CONSTRUCTION. BUILT UNDER COMMAND 14 ARMY GROUP ROYAL ENGINEERS BY 12 CORPS TROOPS RE COMPRISING

262 FIELD COMPANY RE 263   FIELD COMPANY RE   280 FIELD COMPANY RE.   265 FIELD PARK COMPANY RE WITH DETACHMENTS 112 W.K.S.P. AND PKCOYRE   116 RDCONSTR.COYRE.   861 MECH. EQPT COY RE.   965 LT.W.T.OP.CCY   297 COY RASC (GT) 1636 RASC PL. (FBE) AND 1077 COY (GT) BELGE.'

The reader to whom this long list of units of the Royal Engineers may be meaningless must understand that one dare not omit them. Those numerals and abbreviations enshrine the identification of thousands of sappers who, among a medley of other death-defying duties, built bridges with their blood.

One of the troubles about finding things of general interest to write about the sappers is that their personal exploits, so rich in incident and excitement when one uncovers the detail, are rarely recorded. Their archives are more concerned with discussing the technicalities of bridging problems than with the abstractions of their courage, humour, and heroic human endeavour which made impossible missions possible.

They are a special breed, not given to self-seeking publicity or concerned, at least overtly, with what the public relations pundit might term a favourable corporate image. Their long history and great traditions one feels should speak eloquently for themselves. Yet it is a fact that of all the arms of the services the Royal Engineers are in many ways the most taken for granted and least appreciated, certainly as far as the general public is concerned. It would seem that the vast number of duties they perform, the incredible variety of assignments they undertake, dilute any possibility of an integrated impact.

True, now and again, the skill and bravery of their bomb-disposal units propel them into the temporary limelight, when an unexploded bomb unearthed accidentally by a shaken workman on a building site for example, has to be defused. But basically they are a hardy, heroic, pragmatic lot, who, as their history shows, are used to having all sorts of jobs and roles flung at them.

In 1987 they celebrated the bi-centenary of being given the title 'Royal', converting the Corps of Engineers to the more prestigious Corps of Royal Engineers. But long before this overdue recognition was bestowed, their origins can be traced back to Norman times since when there have always been engineers helping military operations by making fortifications, earthworks, and tunnels, and maintaining supply routes. So versatile and resourceful did they become that it is not surprising that they were the progenitors of many outstanding developments in our military organization. Yet few outside the Corps are aware or appreciative of them.

For example they pioneered submarine mining for over 30 years before the Royal Navy took it over in 1905. They were responsible for military mechanical transport for many years before this became progressively the province of the Royal Army Service Corps in 1910. They embraced military flying for a long time until this embryo, whose horizons could not be foreseen and are still limitless, became the legendary Royal Flying Corps just before World War I. Believe it or not, but they were also responsible for the early development and operational use of one of war's most awesome weapons—invented by the British and now an essential part of the world's armies—namely the tank. When tanks were first used in action in numbers at the Battle of Cambrai in 1917, they were commanded by an officer of the Royal Engineers.

But this is not all. They took under their wing military signalling for the 60 years before the Royal Corps of Signals was formed in 1920. Again they nursed and developed the searchlight equipment and units until, as a logical step to have them working in tandem with our guns, they were finally taken over by the Royal Artillery. They were involved with transport operating and movement-control services from as far back as 1882 until the Royal Corps of Transport absorbed these functions in 1965.

Their motto, 'UBIQUE—QUO FAS ET GLORIA DUCUNT', inspired one wit to remark as he drove in his jeep along a perilous road which was being worked on by scores of sweating sappers, 'not only are these bloody engineers ubiquitous—but they are every-bloody-where as well—thank God'.

So far, I have dealt mainly with some of the exploits of the Royal

Engineers, but the contribution to the Bailey story made by Canada and the United States of America was outstanding, each in its own right and individual way. The next chapters will show something of the amazing enterprise and devotion which the Bailey inspired them to achieve.

9 An Engineer's War

BECAUSE the mobility of armies in World War II was the key to victory as demonstrated by the Germans' blitzkrieg in 1940 and the final surge of the Allies over the Rhine in 1945, the worldwide conflict has often been described as an 'engineer's war'. This is undoubtedly true. No matter how partisan one might be for any particular arm of any of the services, one has to acknowledge that the sappers of every nation came into their own on a par with the front-line fighting infantry as the 'queen of the battle'.

This was because never before in the history of warfare was so much demolition experienced, so much damage inflicted on lines of communication, and so much disruption of supplies as on the scale inflicted by the Germans in retreat. The vast advance in the technology and power of explosives since World War I inherent in the mines that were laid, the shells fired by heavy guns, and the bombs dropped by aircraft gave the Germans, and subsequently the Japanese, an awesome capacity for the destruction of docks, railways, roads, and most important of all, the vital bridges, regardless of their size.

It is instructive, therefore, to explain in general terms the problems which other nations faced in determining how to make an assault across a river where the bridge had been blown. This was a challenge common to all, but the answers evolved in different ways according to national attitudes and state of pre-war preparedness.

The Corps of Engineers of the United States numbered half a million officers and enlisted men by the Spring of 1945, about eight per cent of their total army. When compared with the fact that between 1939 and 1941 the number of enlisted men increased from 6000 to almost 70,000 one can gauge the gigantic leap to the 1945 figures which reflected the importance of the 'engineer's war'. Like the engineers of the British and other armies they had a host of tasks. To be specific, here is a list of a few of them at random.

From the outset many of the Corps were laying down or repairing the strips at improvised airfields, and building or rebuilding hangars and barracks. They were also erecting everything from offices to latrines at innumerable military bases. They were enlarging or maintaining the endless network of tracks and highways. Some were installing and operating miles and miles of pipelines for petroleum. Combat engineers were clearing minefields, digging drains, building bridges, and clearing roads and rubble. Still other engineers were driving bulldozers, building railways, manning boats, making maps, purifying water, forging and shaping steel, and running sawmills. In all areas of battle, from the front line to rear bases, the engineers were at work on a thousand tasks.

The US Corps of Engineers has a long and proud history. In 1950 it celebrated its 175th anniversary, thus honouring the date of one Richard Gridley who was appointed Chief Engineer of the Revolutionary forces in 1775. Just like the British, the state of their bridging, however, in terms of suitability for a war of quick manoeuvre and mobility which was demonstrated by the Germans in 1940 was, to put it mildly, not encouraging.

Reports about the German blitzkrieg demonstrated that this spectacular breakthrough was backed by unprecedented strength in engineering support. Each panzer division had a large engineer battalion consisting of three companies, each of many hundreds of highly trained men, supported by a bridge train. With their speed of advance they often seized bridges before they could be demolished by the demoralized French and British forces. But whenever the bridges were blown in time, the Germans had well-rehearsed answers. They built rafts on pneumatic floats which were easy to transport 'flat-packed' and simple to inflate when required. Grouped closed together in various permutations according to load requirements these rafts could carry tons of vehicles, guns, equipment, and men in any direction. The rafts were guided by soldiers paddling from the comfortable seats provided by sitting on the edge of these giant air-filled floats.

To carry their tanks over a river they used rubber boats and pontoons to provide the buoyancy in supporting a 'treadway' which spanned the river. Although the concept was not new the Germans made it a practical innovation. Normally, when one thinks of a floating bridge, one envisages the pontoons being covered by a continuous form of decking or roadway having adequate tolerance of width to provide for any reasonable irregularity in the vehicle's movement.

This treadway was simply two narrow pathways made of steel, such as one sees nowadays when driving a car up a ramp, but which were wide enough for wheels or tracks of different vehicles to be accommodated. They were made in prefabricated sections and were joined together in a special way to prevent the bobbing boats from breaking them. It can be seen that by having just two strips along which the driver could guide his wheels or tracks it was no longer necessary to build the standard roadway over the greater width of the pontoons. Consequently the tread-way version gave much greater speed in construction.

Once across the river the Germans dismantled their equipment and sent it forward again to support the combat troops. They then replaced it with a standard girder bridge as time was no longer of the essence. The latter in terms of flexibility and simplicity of erection never matched the Bailey. Enemy experts never had a chance to examine the Bailey from which they would assuredly have learnt a great many lessons, because when the Bailey was used in Europe in 1943 the Germans were retreating and the Allies were advancing.

Contrary to the popular opinion that the 1940 blitzkrieg was achieved by a heavily mechanized German army, my researches revealed that this was simply not the case. This lightning war of movement, dramatized by German propaganda film of tanks and half-track vehicles charging across Europe, conjures up a vision of victorious battles in which the German soldier just enjoyed the ride. Although they had a great deal of fine armour and fine weapons at that time, most of the German army, and especially their engineers, were not tank-borne and were lucky even to get a ride in a truck.

They relied heavily on the well-developed European rail network to move divisions into the battle areas. The majority then had to foot-slog up to the front or use bicycles and motorcycles. Horses were also available in large numbers, especially for the officers. So the life of the German engineer as regards comfort and conveyance was perhaps not so well catered for as his counterpart in the Allied armies who often had armoured scout cars and lorries in which to travel.

The front-line engineers, rejoicing in the German polysyllabic word 'Panzerpionierbataillon,' were ingenious in finding ways to effect minor crossings in the event of major water obstacle absorbing all their standard equipment of rubber boats and pontoons. Improvization was then an alternative which they pursued with the fanatical thoroughness which characterizes so many activities of that resourceful race. They would literally take anything which came to hand which would float. Any old boats or timber, empty petrol cans, or oil drums were all pressed into service in order to contrive some sort of bridge. They built massive girder structures to keep their railway lines working, and they had a variety of bridging systems which used permutations of steel members, but these were all nut-and-bolt jobs, both tedious and tiresome, unlike Bailey's simple panel-and-pin principle.

When the Russians learned about the Bailey they were quick to send a delegation to the Italian front to see it in action. Photographs record their visit, and reports confirmed that they were immensely impressed as they had nothing to compare with it. However events conspired to relegate their potential use of it to an unfulfilled option. The reason was simple. When the Russians surged forward they used rafts and pontoon bridges to establish ever-bulging bridgeheads as the Germans withdrew, and there was time to follow up with their standard line-of-communication girder bridges without fear of interruption.

Reflecting on the lessons of the blitzkrieg, a high-ranking officer of the Corps of Engineers of the US Army wrote: 'Does an unfordable river block the advance? Perhaps a critical bridge may be seized by the dash of a few motorcyclists while the defenders are still hesitating to destroy it. But suppose the bridge is out, the opposite bank still held by the enemy? Time was when the army waited until night, crossed in the dark by raft or skiff, gained a foothold on the opposite bank . . . later built a bridge. Now it appears that success may sometimes be achieved more speedily—a crossing accomplished audaciously in fast motorboats, or a bridge built under fire.' The last few words anticipated the hope that such a bridge might yet be found.

The Americans faced the same anxieties and problems about their bridging as the British did. They had to find an all-purpose bridge, flexible, simple to erect and to strengthen at will, and easy to transport. These attributes they found difficult to reconcile at first. So they devised three versions of pontoon and fixed bridges: one to cover the initial assault, one for combat support in which they had a little more time, and finally, when the battle had moved on, one as a line-of-communication bridge which was a more permanent and stronger structure. The last was available in two versions of portable steel bridges modelled on British designs before the Bailey came into existence.

Then, just like the British, their calculations and equipment were confounded by the news in May 1940 that they had to accommodate a growing family of heavier tanks. These were required in the light of information about the superior weight of German armour. A period of mend and make-do ensued as they experimented with improved versions of their existing pontoon techniques and materials.

In December 1940 something happened which directed their thoughts to the efficacy of the steel treadway bridge which the Germans were using. US sappers were putting on a night show for the magazine *Newsweek* cameramen by building a pontoon bridge. A tank was backed on to it to give the photographers some action shots. When the driver tried to move forward off the bridge, the engine stalled. A bulldozer was summoned and only succeeded in budging it. The end pontoon sank to the bottom of the river, the tank was backed-up a bit, and soon most of the bridge was under water. The tank sank with the driver escaping to safety. But when the tank was lifted from the river bed it was found not to be a nine-ton as was expected but a 13-ton model, considerably heavier than the capacity of the bridge. It was found too that when the tank backed up, the driver had got off centre, thus causing an imbalance which treadways as guiding lines could have avoided.

So the replacement of standard wooden flooring by the steel treadway, closely following the German design, became a priority. But these narrow steel ribbons snaking over the pontoons were flat and in view of the heavier tanks being built it was decided to have treads with the edges raised to prevent the tracks of vehicles slipping out of line. At the same time the notion of having pneumatic boats was metaphorically floated and later adopted.

In December 1941 a significant test took place at Ford Benning, Georgia. The erection of two modes of bridging was set up under strictly comparable conditions. It took 245 sappers four and a half hours to put across the Chattahoochee River a 25-ton pontoon bridge just over 100 yards (90 metres) long. By happy contrast it took 154 sappers, nearly 100 less, to build their new pneumatic-float treadway bridge of 30-ton capacity, an increase of 20 per cent, only two and a half hours to span the same distance. This treadway triumph had a cautionary postscript. One of the senior officers witnessing the event said 'We've adopted something without a real service test'. Less than a year later this was to prove unhappily prophetic.

The American engineers battled on brilliantly against the ever-growing bureaucracy, the ever-growing weight of tanks they had to cater for, and the ever-growing doubts they themselves entertained about providing a multiplicity of bridges. The British by contrast were now unique in working virtually towards a single bridge solution for all seasons and for all reasons: the magical Meccano of the Bailey. It was strikingly different from any American military bridge simply because most of its structure was above rather than below the roadway it provided. In short, the Americans supported their bridges with pontoons from underneath. The British supported theirs with girders aligned just a little below the surface of the decking with the panels rising nearly five feet (1.5 metres) above or nearly up to fifteen feet (4.5 metres) above when panel storeys had to be added.

In February 1942 the US military chiefs stated that they placed their main reliance still on the 30-ton Sherman tank, so the American engineers started perfecting their floating equipage designed for 30-ton loads, including the steel treadway bridges, which the Sherman had already used successfully on several occasions. Enthusiasm for this mode of river crossing had increased even more as a result.

An invasion of Europe was being planned to take place in 1943 and news arrived that the American sappers stationed in Britain who were expected to participate in the assault might prefer the floating Bailey Bridge. Although such a choice was not illogical in view of the Battle of the Atlantic and shortage of cargo space for transporting components from the USA, a prominent member of the US Corps warned against a hasty decision. He said: 'My tour of duty in England last summer taught me that the British are overly optimistic, not only on the capabilities of their own equipment, but also in their production planning. They are prone to seize admitted advantages and extrapolate unwarranted conclusions with a complete disregard for various disadvantages. Based on my observation, I strongly recommend against complete reliance upon the British to meet all of our bridge requirements.'

A further discussion between this officer and the chief of the USA's II Corps Engineers in England confirmed their agreement that the Bailey's usefulness was confined to rear locations!

With hindsight it is almost laughable to reflect on such an outrageously incorrect analysis but then it was 1942 and the Bailey, although tested, had not gone into action. Engineers are an independent, cool, objective, brainy and articulate breed who have to be cautious. Over the centuries they build for ever because the lives of so many, and their manner of living, depend upon their meticulous appraisal of what makes a bridge.

In the autumn of 1942, however, the American engineers faced a number of disasters which, coupled with the news that tanks were to become heavier and wider, tested to the limit their undoubted expertise. Four serious accidents occurred, all on treadway bridges which earlier had been so acclaimed. The first happened when a medium tank was crossing the turbulent Colorado River. It had nearly reached the bank when its tracks began to climb the edge of the treadway. This displacement caused the bridge to tilt, the tank fell on its side into the water, and three floats slid out from under the bridge. No lives were lost.

The second accident took place on the fast-flowing Chattahoochee. The spacing of tanks while crossing the water was the subject of an experiment. When this was cut to 20 yards (18 metres), the floats submerged, the bridge twisted, and two floats slid away. Again no lives were lost, but one tank went under the water while being towed to the shore.

The third accident was the worst. During a training exercise by an armoured division in Tennessee, tanks were crossing a bridge over the Cumberland River. For some reason one driver stopped and another closed in about 15 yards (14 metres) behind. This section of the bridge then submerged, twisting counter-clockwise. Five or six floats were swept away. Both tanks were thrown into the water and six men drowned.

A further tragedy took place at the same site over the Cumberland River as the first test to discover the cause of the others. A tank was driven on purpose with its right track scraping the raised edge of the treadway. At no time did the tank treads climb this small rampart. However, perhaps because of this it had to be a little off centre for some time. The fourth and fifth floats started to submerge. The seventh and eighth floats started to go under. A few floats on and it was seen that the water was now touching the bottom edge of the treadways. The bridge, losing its stability and buoyancy, was now starting to list. The driver was ordered to accelerate his tank to see if the list could be corrected. Instead the list was accentuated.

The driver was ordered to leave the tank immediately. A horrifying spectacle ensued. He made three efforts to come out of the open driver's hatch but was somehow unable to shake himself free. He was almost completely out by the time the tank entered the water, but he was not seen again. As we have seen, bridging is a risky business and here again the old adage that every bridge demands a life was re-affirmed.

Confusion, consternation, and arguments were expressed in an exchange of memoranda between high-ranking officers. Eventually the resultant modifications from the lessons which had been learned in such a hard way gave the treadway bridge its final certificate of trustworthiness.

But by then, news of a further increase in the weight and width of heavier tanks came as a shock to the US Corps of Engineers who had had reassurance that the Sherman would be standard for some time. This development would affect drastically every bridge they had. The treadway bridge as such had reached its practical limit at 35 tons. The British Churchill tank and its proposed American equivalent would be a 45-ton load.

Now the Bailey bridge, which had partial acceptance as a replacement for the US engineer's girder bridges, started to gain more popularity, but not without reservations, as a floating bridge. The American version of the Bailey and its production together with their improved treadway bridge became vital components in the Americans' victory march in all theatres of war.

Two simple sentences from the archives of the Corps of Engineers of the US Army summarize the years of stress and success:

'Perhaps the Engineer Board . . . was slow to grasp the potentialities of the Bailey and treadway bridges, and to discard other, less suitable types.'

'With the treadway bridge and the Bailey—both radical departures from proven designs—the British and American troops kept pressing hard at the enemy's heels.'

The one intractable problem never solved was to make all parts of the Bailey equally interchangeable between the British and American versions. The difference in production methods in general and the gauges determining the ultra-precision of measurements in particular, were not reconciled, at least not in time to affect the issue. So in 1944 the American Engineers bought nearly a thousand Bailey bridges from their own factories. This was more than sufficient to meet their overseas demands but the American Baileys had to be carefully segregated in Europe to ensure that the parts did not get mixed up with the look-alike British originals.

The zeal and zest with which the Americans set to in producing their Baileys deserves a chapter of its own. It combines some factual and fascinating insight of the might of their collective muscle with their tribute to the man who invented the bridge they so eagerly adopted.

10 'Make It Good. Your Son May Have to Use It'

A S I write I have in front of me a faded but impressive album of photographs and press cuttings. In letters of white and gold on the light green cover within a decorative oval are the words 'US Tour of SIR DONALD BAILEY October 1946'. It was presented to him to mark the occasion by The Engineer Board, Fort Belvoir, Virginia, USA.

To appreciate the significance of this gesture one has to go back to 1941 when an order was placed by the Corps of Engineers of the United States Army for a sample of the Bailey Bridge. They had good reason to do so because, as previously explained, their bridging equipment at the point of their entry into the war in December 1941 was in some ways even more inadequate than that of the British at the start of their war two years before. The Americans faced all the problems imposed by modern warfare of carrying heavy load tonnage, speed of erection, and flexibility. Their standard method of putting decking on top of pontoons for river crossings in the context of the new requirements proved to be unsatisfactory. But they are wonderful people for moving fast once they recognize what has to be done. This is well illustrated by their positive reaction to the sample they examined and their brilliant co-ordination and mass production of their own version of the Bailey when they enlisted their vast industrial power.

A story much retold during the war, and utterly apocryphal, illustrates delightfully the 'get up and go' of American philosophy. An order was given to accelerate the increase of their merchant fleet. So they went to work. As a result they conjured up so many of their multi-purpose 'Liberty' ships at such a pace off the assembly line that they were fast running out of candidates to perform the launching ceremonies. At one time it is related when the speed of their production was at its height the wife of the local Congressman was called upón to do the honours. She stepped on to the platform with her entourage. A bottle of champagne was pressed into her hand all ready with festive ribbon to be flung against the bow of the ship after the immortal words 'I name this ship Liberty Bell, etc' were spoken. She then exclaimed with understandable surprise as she surveyed the empty dock 'but where is she?' There was a moment's silence. Then from way down below on the dockyard floor the voice of a sweating riveter, fraught with urgency, bellowed 'start swinging, lady'.

And so it was that with similar energy they set about producing their officially named 'Portable Panel Bridge' but which they still called in everyday parlance, as all the other nations did, the 'Bailey Bridge'.

The first major difficulty which they encountered was reconciling the numerous differences between the dimensions of the ordinary run-of-the-mill standard structural steel sections of the Americans and those of the British. So their design of the Bailey panel was modified to accommodate American Standards. The attempt to achieve interchangeability with British parts was a most complicated and tedious process because in lay terms it meant that even the tiniest fraction of an inch in difference between the American and British standard measurements would result in a niggling misfit as futile as trying to match the proverbial square peg with a round hole.

Representatives of the major steel mills were summoned urgently for consultation to work out what kind of steel should be used to give the required strength for the panels but involving the minimum of materials vital to other production needs of the war effort.

It is hard to believe but within a few months, early in 1942 in fact, three companies from the many briefed were awarded contracts by the Corps of Engineers to build the American version of Bailey bridges. They were the Detroit Steel Products Company of Detroit, The Commercial Shearing and Stamping Company of Youngstown, and The American Elevator Company of Louisville. They had an awesome task because nothing like the Bailey Bridge had ever been handled before. Confusion and upheaval rocked their plants. New shop lay-outs had to be installed. Existing machines had to be converted. Jigs, gauges, raw materials, and new buildings had to be catered for. Detailed plans and a torrent of blueprints were drawn up, revised, and drawn up again far into the winter nights.

Co-operation between the three firms themselves and with the Corps of Engineers moved mountains like magic. There were frequent conferences at the War Department in Washington and at Fort Belvoir where the British parts were examined minutely. It was then that the spirit of co-operation blossomed to ensure the success of the project.

The three contracting firms, or perhaps in another sense more aptly described as the three expanding firms, gathered in informal talks. They sought advice from each other about disposing of individual problems. They exchanged technical tips. They scouted and arranged mutual sources of supply. They did not neglect, of course, to send a representative to England to see what could be learnt about the manufacture of the Bailey in that by now war-torn and blitzed island.

He was Mr Heems, General Superintendent of the Commercial Shearing and Stamping Company and I am indebted to Mr R. S. Bishop and Mr K. S. Frazier, joint authors of an article in a June 1945 issue of the USA publication *The Military Engineer*, for succinctly describing his dilemma. You will recall that Britain had to involve hundreds of small firms not needed for other vital war production to make parts for the bridge, whereas America with its gigantic resources only had to go initially to three companies already expert in compatible engineering.

They reported that 'Since it is the custom in the British system of contracting for each fabricator to make only one or a few items for an assembly, Mr Heems had to travel the length and breadth of the country, visiting some 300 manufacturers of component parts, observing panel pins at one place and end posts at another. He found that each of these companies shipped their parts to a central depot where complete sets containing the correct quantities of each item were made up and prepared for shipment to the field.'

One can imagine how tedious and frustrating it must have been for Mr Heems combatting the black-out, the vagaries of the British Railways' otherwise splendid war-time schedules, and locations all over the United Kingdom, in his search for all the parts.

He was assisted by Stair Stewart who accompanied him on visits to a number of locations where components of the Bailey were made. This was in August 1942 when the extended daylight hours had eased the problems of travel and production. Heems, somewhat bewildered by the many diversified sources of manufacture for the bits and pieces of the Bailey, doubtless reflected this in his reports.

It was not surprising, therefore, that the US Corps of Engineers decided to make general contractors responsible for the fabrication of complete Bailey Bridge sets. Each company would undertake to produce the entire panel system from raw material to finished job within its own precincts and resources.

Stair Stewart recalled that the person at HQ of the US Corps of Engineers who was among the first to recognize the value of the Bailey, and who promoted its adoption enthusiastically at the highest levels of the Corps was Colonel Frank Besson. It was he who did much to give momentum to the acceptance and manufacture of the Bailey in the USA, resulting in rapid expansion of factories involved.

As more contracts were placed, new contractors entered the field. Ceco Steel Products Company of Chicago, The International Steel Company of Evansville, and the Virginia Bridge Company of Roanoke accepted portions of the work. Here were former competitors in the industrial field now working shoulder to shoulder on the same project, each attempting in a new competitive spirit to be the first to suggest improvements of materials and methods to the others. Each plant was open at all times to delegations from the other companies. Fixture designs, sequence of operations, plant layouts, and packing methods were exchanged freely.

As some of the sources of material could not produce fast enough to meet the pace of the work, which was stepped up to fever pitch, it was found necessary to exchange raw materials and equipment so that all manufacturers could meet their schedules. Many small industries were called on to produce stampings, castings, bolts, pins, wrenches, and other items. All responded willingly so that the American Engineers were promptly achieving the production of what they described as 'one of the vital weapons of the war, a speedy link in transportation of troops, mechanized weapons, and supplies. Its potentialities were recognized in design and the bridge exceeded all expectations in the field'.

More orders followed as the battlefields in Europe and in the Pacific were enlarged and production had to be doubled and tripled, until in 1945 sets (each of about 95 tons of bridge material) were following each other from the assembly lines with clockwork regularity.

The American bridge set comprised a mind-boggling kit of some 36,607 separate pieces not including many other items like bolts, rods, and boxes used in packing. This set provided enough materials for what a sapper would call a 'double double' construction capable of spanning 150 feet (46 metres). A 'double double' in simple terms is a Bailey bridge, the sides of which are two panels wide and two panels high. Of course with this amount of material, each set could provide a variety of bridges of different spans and load capacity.

Although statistics can be boring, one can hardly demonstrate effectively the massive American production power without using them. By the end of the war in Europe nearly 4,000 of these sets (each of about 35,000 pieces) were produced in the USA at the rate of about 20 sets per week or over 1,000 sets per year, representing nearly one million tons of material and nearly 4,000 miles (about 6,400 km) of welding.

But although the statistics enable one to 'feel the width', so to speak, of this non-bespoke bridge, one has to 'mind the quality' even more. Engineers of distinction the world over are a special breed whose care, precision, and quality have to dominate their thinking. One false assumption or slip of the slide rule can cost vast sums of money, waste months of fruitless time, and even bring a bridge down. The Americans gave their hearts as well as their minds to the motivation of their workforces in producing the best possible components. At one assembly line at the International Steel Company plant, Evansville, Indiana, there was a thoughtful notice which read 'Make it good. Your son may have to use it.' Another in the same factory read: 'Hurry it up. Finish on time. They want our bridge, to cross the Rhine'.

The American soldiers loved that bridge. They built and travelled over it on the roads to Messina, on the roads to Rome, and on and over the ravines and rivers of Normandy, and on to the roads of the Ruhr. Ernie Pyle, the great American reporter ranking first among equals of all the best-known Allied war correspondents, wrote of the 'wonder bridge each one of which is named as it is erected by the engineers, just as it is customary to name a bomber or a pet!'

Delving into American archives, several interesting snippets emerge which complement the story of the prodigious production effort of the USA. It answers the question about how their symbolic 'son' did in fact use the Bailey once it was delivered 'good' and 'on time to cross the Rhine'. If one considers that careful painstaking preparation is essential for the success of any project then this must rank as a five-star example.

Lt Colonel William J. Irby commanded the 148th Engineer Combat Battalion of the United States Army. He and his men had not only been studying and thinking about putting a Bailey over the Rhine nine months before they got to it, but seven months beforehand, way back in September 1944, they had started practising for it on the River Meuse.

All through the autumn and winter of 1944 the practice sessions went on. Weeks after they were over, and when a lull in the operations permitted, a platoon or company was sent back on a refresher course to check and go through their bridge-building exercise yet again. They had now reached a pitch where each platoon could build a floating section in only 30 minutes. So when the great day arrived in March 1945 for the men of the 148th to swing into action, the equipment must have been so familiar that the Bailey panels looked like intimate friends of the family at home with their slippers on.

Their task was to build a floating Bailey of well over 1,000 feet (300 metres) north of Remagen, and they had the assistance of some other units to beef up the numbers available for this daunting assignment. Their transport was also fortified by the addition of 114 2½-ton trucks and four cranes. In engineering terms the words of the Civil War general Nathan Bedford Forrest who allegedly said in effect that to win a battle 'you get there first with the most' was still the policy.

They got off to a flying start because the factor which contributed most to the speed of getting the equipment down and into place was the ordered way in which all the bits and pieces were neatly laid out prior to the move. This was done with minute attention to detail and forethought. Each and every part of the bridge was grouped so that the item which had to be first out of a lorry was the last one loaded. Similarly the part over which all the other parts took precedence was the first one in. Anybody who has packed the boot of a car with the family essentials for a long holiday, or loaded a pantechnicon when moving house, will get the idea. It was a massive and methodical piece of organization, putting hundreds of components together in the right order to eliminate delays and mitigate any mix-up.

Work then began on clearing the construction sites, on building no less than 16 floating sections, unloading the countless boats for the entire job, and preparing two landing bays and two landing-bay piers. There was enough work to keep building contractors busy for weeks. But this was chicken-feed for the well-drilled US engineers responding to their months of preparation and rehearsal.

What was not so easy was holding this tenuous 40 yard (36 metre) long floating bridge in position. How could one anchor it securely against the swift current of the racing Rhine? It was March, and the melting waters from distant icy mountains was accelerating its momentum. So this is what they did.

Rhine barges are enormous and carry vast cargoes. Two of the largest were selected, filled to the brim with rocks, and sunk by using small charges of dynamite. Three stout cables were then attached to each of them and in turn to the bridge. In addition five 1550 lb (680 kg) anchors were also used to hold it. To assist with the operation one Lt Benjamin F. Thomas, who had previously trained like so many others in the River Meuse exercises, found and repaired four tug-boats which helped to tow the floating sections into place while US Naval craft did the main work.

With such well organized and improvised activity, a job that would normally take weeks, if not months, was completed in 47 hours and 45 minutes. The total length of the bridge finally was some 1,250 feet (380 metres). That is equivalent to four soccer pitches laid end to end.

Colonel Irby received a telephone call which pleased him. It was from his superior who said that this was 24 hours quicker than the most optimistic estimate entertained at HQ.

As an enlightening revelation about how the US engineers, indeed the engineers of any army, can have their role misunderstood, I will mention one particular incident. At the end of an icy January in 1944 the US sappers set about building a big Bailey, the sides of which were three panels wide and two panels high (a 'double-triple') across a river on the Belgian-German border. This was to enable the famous US 82d Airborne Division to be transported forward.

It was snowing like hell, and blustering winds brought blizzards sweeping in with blinding ferocity. Enemy shellfire added to the hazards. But they worked every hour, day and night, defying the appalling conditions and with only their heart and spirit to keep them warm. After 40 hours of continuous struggle they finished their mammoth job and then went on to sweep the approaches further back for mines and to clear them of the snow with their bulldozers. Utterly spent, red-eyed, and sore, hiding their seared hands under their armpits for warmth, they cast their exhausted gaze on the convoy of lorries carrying the 82d Division over their bridge.

The occupants, tucked up comfortably in their vehicles, had not witnessed the torture of the operation which enabled them to cross an icy river without getting their feet wet. Otherwise the stinging words of one paratrooper seeing the immobile engineers standing by, would not have been said. He leaned out as his lorry reached the bridge and shouted: 'Why the hell don't you rear echelon bastards ever come up front and fight?'

The respect for the Bailey to which the Americans made such an outstanding contribution was typified by the generous admission of the chief engineer of the US 5th Army in Italy. He said quite simply it was 'the most useful all-purpose fixed bridge in existence'.

More fulsome was the appreciation expressed by Lt Colonel Bruce W. Reagan of the US Corps of Engineers who described it as 'Sir Donald Bailey's little gem'. .

The Colonel went into action with the US engineers for the invasion of Europe, and was constantly struck by the way this 'little gem' provided the permanence, the durability, and the dazzling versatility of the multi-faceted diamond. He pointed out that the bridge, the Sherman tank, and the Douglas aircraft were credited by President Eisenhower as being the major equipment factors leading to the 1945 victory in Europe.

Among the testimonies the Colonel cited for its battle-worthiness and flexibility is one equally remarkable for showing the bravery of the US Sappers who built it. He said: 'A shrouding fog lifted on the Saar River one December morning of 1944 to reveal a thing of beauty—not one that Picasso would admire but perhaps the more pragmatic Leonardo da Vinci would have appreciated. It was one of Sir Donald Bailey's bridges with Sherman tanks rolling across, and its elegance lay not in symmetry of visual impact but in its utility. An unusual appearance, it had one side higher than the other—hardly what one would expect of a bridge. Its charm lay in the indestructible quality that Sir Donald built into his product, and was only one of the many virtues it had displayed'.

The fog had obscured the bridge for a few extra hours from enemy observation, during which time the work done on it had resulted in an unsightly version of its usual pleasing symmetry. To put it mildly it had not been a pleasant night for the Americans.

Unlike many, the site was not protected by stone houses nearby and was within range of the heavy guns of the Siegfried Line artillery. The bridge was damaged to the point of being able to carry only its own weight before completion. The fog of that morning permitted time to file off the jagged edges and add more panels for reinforcement. The tanks got across. This 16-hour bridging day had started at dusk after a few troops had worked their way across a flooded plain and the river to the village on the far bank. It took no genius on the part of the enemy to realize that something in the way of bridging was to take place that night. A diversionary effort in the form of raft construction, hopefully to draw some of the artillery fire, was started a mile downstream. It did not work. Any time a crew started on the bridge, the area was blanketed with shellfire from the Siegfried Line, forcing the men to disperse. Several hours of this and it was concluded that someone was within sound of the action and was relaying timing data to the artillery controllers. Once all the villagers on the far side were rounded up and placed under guard, the firing became less effective. A recently occupied foxhole found on the far bank after daylight confirmed the suspicion.

The next day some special and much heavier equipment arrived that was designed especially for close assaults on the Siegfried Line. The normal loading was the 35-ton Sherman tank but now there was a tank mounted with a steel chain flail to clear mine-fields and a self-propelled 155mm gun, both weighing 55 tons each. More panels were added to strengthen the existing Bailey and they crossed safely.

Colonel Reagan mentioned several other examples from his bridging repertoire. On the side of a deep mountain gorge a culvert had been blown leaving no space for the normal counterweight needed to launch the bridge across the 120-foot (37-metre) gap. So he brought up a bull-dozer and sat it on the bit of the Bailey that had been completed. The bulldozer was then moved back inch by inch as the panels were pushed across to meet the far abutment.

At a town called Ettelbruck, a name derived from Etzel, the German for Attila the Hun, a four-track railway overpass joined by a linking pier to a smaller river pier had been destroyed. One normally envisages a Bailey making any crossing in a nice straight line, but the challenge at Ettelbruck involved both a curving and sloping approach. It would seem that this combination of deflection in height and direction could only be met by rubber panels. But by an ingenious use of the standard steel ones, some stacked upwards and some horizontally and with the whole being anchored by cables to some trees nearby the problem was solved. It is interesting that, when the permanent replacement for this bit of makeshift magic was built, a bronze statue no less than 8 feet (2 metres) high, of General Patton pointing dramatically into Germany alongside a Sherman tank, was unveiled. But this was not the famous 'Patton' Bridge to be referred to later, the building of which was again a masterpiece.

'The Bailey Bridge was—and indeed remains, a little gem' concluded Colonel Reagan. His use of the present tense was to remind one that to this day most state highway departments in the USA and in countless countries, keep Bailey equipment for emergencies. But all this is the subject of another chapter.

11 Maple Leaf Magic

AT a time when help was desperately needed, when Britain stood alone, and was in danger of being invaded by the victorious German army, Canada rose once more magnificently to the occasion as she had done in World War I. By that hot summer of 1940 she had already landed on English soil her 1st Canadian Infantry Division.

An essential part of it was the Division's engineering companies. They spent months and months thereafter in constant training which had to be carried out with old-fashioned pontoon and box-girder bridges because there was then nothing else to practice with. A box-girder bridge was a rectangular see-through structure, about the same proportions as a shoe-box, with the edges formed of thick steel girders supported by steel crossbeams. Not easy to handle and not conducive to speed of erection. Floating bridges were much faster to assemble, and it is recorded in the Directorate of History archives in Ottawa that a section of No. 1 Field Company of the 1st Canadian Infantry Division put a 100 foot (30 metre) floating bridge across a small river in 55 minutes, and tore it down again in 49 minutes. While one may say that this was all very well for something done on a suitable site under ideal conditions, it is a matter of pride to record that these Canadian Sappers reproduced comparable and better results in combat later on.

These men were, like sappers everywhere, quite exceptional. They brought technical skills with them from civilian life. Officers with suitable degrees were recruited from the universities, engineering firms, and also from among the other ranks. The latter were taken from many skilled trades including electricians, blacksmiths, fitters, surveyors, plumbers, carpenters, draughtsmen, artificers, bricklayers, masons, and miners. The

94

surge of such men in their Army so early in the war must have bequeathed a new generation of Do-it-Yourself Canadian householders—trying to cope without their usual plumbers, carpenters, or handymen.

In February 1941 the Canadian Sappers noted that a new type of bridge was introduced called the Inglis. Little did they know that the Bailey had just then received the go-ahead for full-scale testing. In fact they complained, not without justification, that the addition of the Inglis (in short supply) left them with too many different kinds of bridges to work on. They now had variations of floating bridges, small box girder bridges, and large box girder bridges. Training old dogs to do new tricks, as well as the raw recruits still arriving from Canada, became a real problem. Fortunately, before many months had passed, help was at hand. The news of the Bailey had arrived.

This came from Major Tregillus, an engineer at Division HQ who was the first Royal Canadian Engineer officer to see this revolutionary structure at Ripon in Yorkshire in the late autumn of 1941. It was soon pronounced as 'one of the most adaptable types of bridging ever conceived' which the Canadians translated in sapper lore in their official history as the 'technical wonder of the Western World'. By June 1942 they were training and experimenting with it madly.

A year later they were in action as part of the invasion of Sicily. Their first Bailey spanning a 40-foot (12-metre) gap was erected under fire in 4½ hours near the town of Leonforte in July 1943. From then on the Canadian sappers went from strength to strength as they gathered battle experience. They were ingenious with their improvisation and ability to increase speed of erection during the arduous Italian campaign.

On one occasion they found a 50-foot (15-metre) gap and only 30 feet (9 metres) of bridge as the balance of the equipment had not caught up with them. So they took all the parts that made up the 'nose' of the bridge to complete the extra 20 feet (6 metres) required. But then as the nose was always pushed out in front to achieve with a counterweight the correct balance to prevent the bridge tipping down into the gap, what was the answer when it was removed? Well, these ingenious Canadians dug out the bank to make it level with the roadway. They built the complete bridge on the near bank and gradually pushed it over the gap using a bulldozer as a huge counterweight on the rear of the bridge. After much time in heaving, shoving, and praying they did the job. They noted two things about this startling departure from conventional procedure. First, they had reached a level of expertise through constant practice that allowed them to improvise from first principles when meeting a problem never envisaged in their training. Secondly, the Bailey bridge itself was versatile enough to allow such improvisation. Another ploy by the Canadians was what they called the 'bridge gallop'. Because the rivers in Italy sometimes involved a series of bridges being put up close together, the plan was to slap them in one after the other at high speed with each platoon leap-frogging over the completed bridges to the next site. In one such scramble they built no less than five bridges one after the other, all of which were operating within 24 hours. On 29 November 1943 one unit reported that it had bridged 18 gaps in five days. That is one on average just under every seven hours. They might complain of having no sleep, no food, no dry clothing, no rest, and no future, but they could not complain about any lack of practice.

In the regimental history of the 85th Canadian Bridge Company which included five platoons specializing in Bailey fixed and pontoon bridging, little gems of philosophy and human interest can be found occasionally in the litany of the chronological and clinical accounts of their battles in northern Europe.

'D' Platoon arrived in France in time to be bombed in Caen, later to take 12 prisoners at Bernay where Rommel had been strafed by Allied fighter planes, later to put up two gigantic bridges over the Seine which involved a continuous 48-hour shift, and then to put up four bridges in less than 12 hours over the River Somme. They kept on building bridges right on over the Rhine, the Weser, the Aller, and last but not least over the final big river, the Elbe. In all they had helped in putting up 71 bridges in action in about 240 days working alongside the British spearhead forces. That on average is about one Bailey every three to four days, and one can only conclude that they must literally have done it in their sleep. Otherwise how could they have had any?

'F' Platoon joined the invasion forces in France in July 1944 and eventually arrived at Falaise, their ranks somewhat depleted owing to frequent bombing by enemy planes en route. However they disported themselves by picking up a small German car only to be told that all enemy equipment had to be turned in. Unperturbed by this contretemps, they immediately bartered the car for five bottles of Calvados and three chickens from a local farmer. It is unlikely that this incident will constitute a stirring chapter in the official history of the war, but the memory of a good chicken dinner with a tasty chaser of Calvados to follow is something those enterprising Canadians are not likely to forget.

They seem to have cultivated a rapport with French farmers and not only in terms of food and drink. On another occasion, having had some attention from snipers, a French farmer told them that German soldiers were in position in the woods close to his buildings. What to do? How many, if the story were true, might be there? Without any palaver, the platoon commander led a patrol of six of his men in a stealthy tour of the trees and undergrowth. They returned unharmed and in triumph with six dejected prisoners. Truly a sapper's life is full of the unexpected.

'G' Platoon also made their move to the battlefront in France in July 1944, but were diverted to Holland. A laconic entry in their diary noted they were 'resting' for three days at Nijmegen but added a few words which somewhat belied this happy experience. 'During this period,' it said, 'the Jerries were shelling and dropping anti-personnel bombs on and all around us. We were also called upon to supply bridging to repair the single span of the Nijmegen-Arnhem bridge which the Jerries were still shelling'.

Some rest that was to be sure. Very little went according to plan, but then, of course, plans in wartime are only made to ensure that the many unexpected departures from them can be identified.

The story of 'H' Platoon is much the same as the others. Although primarily concerned with the floating Bailey — in effect a pontoon platoon — they were rushed off their wheels in ferrying every kind of bridging equipment to forward dumps so that the momentum of the advance could be sustained. They too got to Nijmegen and their succinct dead-pan diary comment about it gives much food for reflection: 'Our stay in that part of the country' it said simply 'was not *interesting* as we were shelled and bombed from every direction'. (The italics are mine). Obviously it takes a lot more than high explosives to arouse the curiosity of the Canadian sapper.

When they got to the Rhine their ability to improvise the answer in response to unexpected demands upon their cuisine was as effective as those experienced with their bridging. During the lengthy period of construction at this mighty river, the platoon was inundated with hungry visitors from other units looking for a snack. One day their assistant cook, one Private Murray, was advised that 15 extra men would be arriving for dinner. He quickly found the solution by shouting to the cook 'Hey Bill, add another bucket of water to the stew — we have more for dinner'.

Another example of a different humour came to me from Captain John Stevenson. He and his friend Bob Snyder, both from Alberta, recalled a critical overnight operation when they were engineers with the 2nd Canadian Army. To speed things up they decided to build from both sides of the Rhine at Emmerich to meet in the middle. Now many, I am sure, have wondered how engineers manage to get great structures to meet exactly in the middle in this sort of situation. There is a niggling sense of wonder about what the consequences might be if they were just a few inches out when it came to the final join. Those digging the tunnel from both sides of the English Channel must have often shared the same kind of thoughts. One can envisage a few inches, even a foot out, but this was ridiculous. Although the alignment was right, Stevenson and Snyder were yards out — they ended up with one bay short in the centre. In recalling it, John Stevenson, with wry self-castigation, added: 'It took some time to bring up the extra bay. Our record time was somewhat spoiled. Our Chief Engineer was very angry. All the medals that we were assigned for this operation were withdrawn as punishment to us. I had even written up the citations.'

Going through the war diaries of the Canadian sappers it is impossible to ignore some of the remarks. They were all handwritten with a brevity which nevertheless stirs the imagination.

'Bridge blown on outskirts of Vinchiaturo (Italy, 16 Oct 1943). Recce by two officers—enemy mortars them and they run for their lives. After dark—all clear—3 pl moves to site and starts preparing bank for 90 foot Bailey under mortar and shellfire (none of them close); Bridging brought up to be unloaded. Shells getting closer and closer. Work interrupted often, but at 0630 bridge checked out—all OK.'

'24 Nov 1943. 190 foot triple single Bailey built overnight in high winds. A bulldozer had to be used to hold the bridge.'

'22 Dec 1943. Near Appolinaro—bridge delayed because bulldozer in taking off topsoil uncovered a couple of springs which turned the site into a mud hole.'

'28 Dec 1943: 3 blown bridges on main road. Recce found by-pass requiring only small Bailey. Bridging started to move up 1730 hrs. Trouble: (1) Mines blown up one truck (2) breakdown of bridging lorry. Bridge completed 0600 29 Dec.'

'27 May 1944: 110 foot triple single Bailey built under shellfire at map ref 606235—5 wounded.'

'5 Dec 1944: attack unsuccessful, so no bridging can be constructed yet. Lt Kline attempted daylight recce of existing bridge aided by a mirror on a long stick for looking over the dyke but snipers made the recce impossible.'

The performance of the Canadian sappers couched modestly in such terse language was the equal of the bravest and best of any engineers anywhere. Their handling of the equipment was foreshadowed by the entry in a unit war diary before they left England: 'Men are interested [in training] for to most of them the equipment is new. We all begin to wonder if there is anything the Bailey cannot do.'

The final paragraph of one unit's war diary ending in April 1945 says it all with impressive simplicity about the great contribution of the Canadian sappers and their beloved Bailey: 'We have done the jobs that were given to us, and at no time were complaints heard from any of those with whom we worked. Many letters of appreciation were received and we were glad to receive them as they showed that the other arms of the service understood our problems and difficulties.'

The chain binding the brotherhood of sappers of every army never had a stronger link than that die-stamped with the Maple leaf.

12 Fêted and Fated

S OME men of only modest attainment have a gift for attracting
constant publicity by virtue of their positive self-assertion and extravert behaviour which engage the attention of the media. Their
ability to make an impact on their circles of influence is founded on their
natural out-going personality. Variously described as being a 'character',
or a 'card', or 'having charisma', they have a knack of acquiring fame
or notoriety as easily as slipping into well-worn shoes.

Donald Bailey was the antithesis of such a man. Neither introvert nor
extravert, he was fated to rank with the anonymous as indicated by his
joining the ranks of the Civil Service. He had no pretensions to self-
advancement. He harboured no particular ambitions. He was happy to
try and do a good job without fuss or personal recognition. His schooldays
were totally unremarkable. His days at Sheffield University were equally
so. He was not even memorable for having a particular mannerism or
any idiosyncrasy, unless one includes his defiance of sartorial elegance
by wearing a plain blue suit on periodic visits to London with a brown
Trilby hat pulled down firmly on his head.

Entrenched in a certain mediocrity of performance he seemed destined
to lead his life in obscurity. That is, until he had the idea for his bridge.
This was to propel him from the ranks of the unknown into the full glare
of the limelight. The Bailey Bridge with its alliterative juxtaposition
suddenly thrust his name dramatically before an appreciative public both
at home and abroad in 1944 in the manner already described.

Some acknowledgement had already come his way by the earlier award
in 1942 of an OBE. Being made an Officer of the Order of the British
Empire was deemed by him to be a tribute to his team rather than a
personal accolade. The latter came later in the form of a knighthood

which he once again was pleased to accept on behalf of his team. He said 'When these honours came my way I was conscious of the great debt I owed to all those at the EBE and to the Royal Corps of Engineers for their marvellous work in making my bridge such a success!'

An award in 1946 which gave him particular pleasure was when the Queen of the Netherlands made him Commander of the Order of Orange Nassau in recognition of the constructive role his bridges played in restoring communications in Holland after the German demolition of dams, canals, and river banks. Another tribute he treasured was a certificate he received from King George VI which recorded that despite his arduous duties and the mind-sapping fatigue of his daily routine, he had served four years and 183 days in the Home Guard.

It has been a matter of considerable regret to me that I met Donald Bailey only five years before he died in his 84th year. It was a casual conversation with Colonel Osborne, an ex-Royal Engineer, in London's Garrick Club in 1980 that reminded me of the Bailey Bridge. Having ascertained that the amazing story of the man and his eternal monument had never been told to the public, I became obsessed with the injustice of it all. Unfortunately various commitments, compounded by domestic considerations and a long illness, prevented me from pursuing the biography with any continuity. I gathered information spasmodically with the help of Donald himself but mainly through Lady Bailey, his son Richard, and the good offices of Sir Ralph Freeman and Stair Stewart whom I have already mentioned.

After such a long lapse of time between his student days at Sheffield University and his final retirement near Bournemouth it was difficult to pick up accurate points of detail from those colleagues who remembered him. Some things which were said to me were modified or invalidated by things which either he told me himself or which were recorded in articles in various publications or verbatim reports of interviews with him. To take one trivial example, he was described in his twenties by one source as having 'flaxen hair', by another source 'sandy brown', and by my most reliable source 'dark curly hair'. This only serves to illustrate the inevitable tricks and conflicts of memory and is unimportant. Actually his hair as a lad was dark brown and straight.

He had an impressive dome-like head and a pallid face which was accentuated by his wearing dark horn-rimmed glasses. His features were regular and ascetic, and he had the gentle air of a scholar, and an expression of indefinable aloofness which his natural courtesy and the flicker of a smile quickly dispelled. I noticed from the photographs of his more active days how he held himself very erect with his head bent just a little to the side, giving the overall effect, accentuated by people of lesser stature around him, that he was very tall. In fact that was not so. He was precisely half an inch under six foot (1.68 metres).

Except on what might be termed fairly formal occasions when he wore his blue suit, his normal dress had the workmanlike combination of tweed jacket and baggy grey trousers. He was fond of sucking his pipe as so many men of a thoughtful, reflective nature tend to do. It accompanied him everywhere. I can envisage him feeling for his pipe any time he had something to think about, which meant it was virtually never out of his hand. He must have clung to it with the same tenacity as that of the ivy to the proverbial wall.

By the end of the war he had assumed responsibility for the EBE as its Director. Before him lay new challenges in his work, new travel, new appointments, and finally the dramas of domestic and personal tragedies which left him physically a broken man and mentally one who languished in comparative isolation.

Perhaps the tribute which thrilled him most was when on 1 July 1947 the Honorary Degree of Doctor of Engineering was conferred upon him by his old University, Sheffield. He told me that 'this was something I treasured because not only was Sheffield my original home but the University's wish to honour me gave me my most prized moment.' It is worth reproducing the Public Orator's speech at the ceremony if only because of its eloquence and gentle humour. The Public Orator (Professor D. Browne) proclaimed:

'When the Allied Armies began to advance in Western Europe, they encountered obstacles of a novel kind, or at least of a novel origin. The power of the Air Force had been so lavishly employed to paralyse the enemy that the resultant destruction bade fair to paralyse ourselves. How Sir Donald Bailey freed us from these self-imposed fetters is common knowledge. The Bailey Bridge, a marvel of lightness and strength, bestrode rivers like magic, and his name was exalted among generals and privates alike.

'Napoleon bade his Marshals ask him for anything but time, and if they did not ask for too much of that, he made them Kings. It passes conjecture what he would have made of Bailey, whose gift to the Allied commands in the field was mobility, which is Time itself. But perhaps a senior officer of the Ministry of Supply can smile at kingdoms.

'Sir Donald Bailey we may claim peculiarly as our own; born in Rotherham, he was a student of this University, where he graduated as Bachelor of Engineering in 1923. We can flatter ourselves by thinking that the training which he received here contributed to his achievement. We hope that the great gifts which helped so notably towards victory in war might be fruitfully employed in the vast tasks of reconstruction.'

The final words of that speech got fresh emphasis when only a few years later Donald Bailey was asked by Harold Macmillan (later Prime Minister and then ennobled as Lord Stockton), who was then Minister of Housing and Local Government, to head a committee to examine ways of speeding up the construction of houses. Following the principles employed in the design of his bridge the committee, in record time for such deliberations, made a number of suggestions based on prefabricated units. Bailey was rewarded by an appreciative letter from the Minister signed in his own hand 'again very many thanks, yours sincerely, Harold Macmillan'. The letter said: 'I am very glad to have the report of your Committee with your letter of 23 December. I have read it with a great deal of interest and have already given instructions for it to be published. . . .

'It was good of you to give so much time to this for I know very well that it adds to the labours of a committee if they have to report quickly. The report will, I feel sure, make a useful contribution towards quickening and cheapening the work on house interiors. . . . Apart from the publicity the report will get when it is published and circulated to local authorities I hope it will be possible to bring some of its recommendations into the Department's Ideal Home Exhibit in March. In this and other ways we shall try to make good use of your Committee's recommendations. . . .'

Fulsome as were the kind words and honours bestowed upon him, he was quite unaware of the enormous impact his name carried, particularly in America. The US Corps of Engineers and the many companies making his bridge were full of admiration. So it was not surprising that when Donald Bailey set foot for the first time in the USA immediately after the war on a fact-finding mission, he was accorded a welcome and acclaim by the fraternity of the Bailey brotherhood over there which must have given him great joy.

His first official visit was to the home of the US Army's Engineer Board at Fort Belvoir in Virginia which had been the focal point and mainspring in getting his bridge adopted by America. 'Here' he told me 'as indeed everywhere I went, such was the rapport and mutual interest between us that I felt I had never left home. We spoke the same language in every respect. My bridge never failed to bring up new talking points when comparing our respective notes.'

I have looked at two dozen photographs recording the high spots and personalities he encountered at each of his destinations. They show a variety of poses, of dress, and of scenarios as he made his inspections and took his notes. But there is one constant in virtually all of them. That is the retention of his sturdy pipe. It is to be seen either in his hand or in his mouth, sometimes in both as he took it out or took a puff. Throughout all his vicissitudes in his long life it must have been his most constant and comforting companion for three score years or more.

While the visit of a distinguished bridging engineer on a technical mission to factories and plants is not normally the sort of subject to arouse the interest of the popular press, his arrival in the various cities excited extensive coverage both in text and pictures. A report in the *Detroit Free Press* carried a large picture of him (with pipe in mouth of course) as he examined a map of the waterfront unfolded by Col. A.E. Riani, Detroit's District Engineer. It was headlined 'Bailey Bridge Inventor Visits Detroit' and the lengthy caption included 'Sir Donald Bailey, originator of the famous Bailey Bridge . . . knighted by King George VI . . . his invention proved of great value to the Allied advance on the continent. . . .'

A longer story in the *Detroit Times* which also printed his picture included the following quotes: 'He stated that he had seen nothing in England to compare with the river traffic, with the exception of the Thames River, and was impressed with the river-front areas which were explained to him with the aid of hydrographic chart.

'In general, American factories are more efficiently run than those in England,' he said. 'One of the blessings of the blitz is that the British are building their factories in more modern ways.'

When he got to St Louis the three major newspapers there accorded him even more column inches. The story in the *St Louis Post Despatch* carries his picture. Once again it is worth quoting at some length if only as an example of accurate factual reporting using indirect speech. There is a large heading:

'DESIGNER OF BAILEY BRIDGE VISITS CITY'

Then there is a daunting subheading for anyone looking for light relief. 'Sir Donald Bailey Discussing Military Construction with Engineers Here.' But the story then picks up with dead-pan recital of facts.

'Sir Donald Bailey, British engineer who designed the Bailey bridge which was widely used in World War II, came to St Louis yesterday with a group of British and American Army engineering officers for conferences with Leif J. Sverdrup and John I. Parcel, local consulting engineers. Sir Donald, who has been associated with the design of every British military bridge produced in the last 18 years, said he was representing the Ministry of Supply on the trip to compare and discuss military building programs of the two nations. He declined to talk about his work in detail because of its confidential nature. He said he had been getting utmost co-operation from representatives of United States military and industrial establishments, who were willing to exchange ideas with their British counterparts without restriction. The steel and light metals industries in this country have been most interesting to him, Sir Donald said. Regarding the bridge which bears his name, he said that since the end of the war it has been used extensively in Germany as a permanent installation, in some cases as long as 1,500 feet [460 metres]. The Bailey bridge was used by British and American engineer troops in the war in temporary installations. It is a prefabricated bridge made of standard panels which can be manufactured in the United States as well as in England and standardized so as to be interchangeable. Sir Donald was knighted this year for his engineering accomplishments.'

Naturally everywhere he went he was revered by the many Americans whose involvement in the 'Portable Panel Bridge' made his a household name. He was met everywhere by high-ranking officers, conducted on

103

VIP tours of the great corporations and construction companies that had contributed to the mass production of what he once simply conceived on the back of an envelope. He was made guest of honour at numerous functions, reflecting the American gift for generous hospitality. Sir Donald left the United States for Canada with a host of happy memories and wads of notes about the things he saw there which later he would put to good use both in memos to the Ministry and in practice when he returned home.

His work at the re-named Military Engineering Experimental Establishment (MEXE) provided new dimensions of productive activity for his team. He bequeathed me a little battered notebook. In it written in his meticulous rounded handwriting (in pencil) was the text of a lecture he gave entitled 'The work of an engineering R and D Establishment'. Extracts from the less technical parts of the dissertation are illuminating, especially as he could never resist leavening any of his talks, no matter the audience, with the yeast of a good story:

'But to come to my own Establishment now called MEXE. This started some time in the 1920s as The Experimental Bridging Establishment and was given the task of designing military bridges since these had special attributes which it was very difficult to persuade Industry to incorporate in any designs suggested by them.

'A number of distinguished soldiers were in charge at one time or another—perhaps Major Martel, later General Martel, was the best known. He was responsible for a number of important developments and some more dicey efforts. There was, for example, the "Stepping Stone" floating bridge which simply consisted of a number of openwork crates, connected by wire ropes. These crates had some flotation but less than would be required to support a vehicle on their own. The idea being that if the vehicle crossed smartly it would be away from any particular spot before it could sink.

'This had worked quite well several times and thought to be of sufficient promise to lay on a high-powered demonstration to the War Office. On the day, the test vehicle got nearly across the river and then got off centre. The crates tipped and the driver got the wind up and stopped. The whole lot sank slowly in an undignified manner. The driver remaining heroically at his post until only his head and shoulders were visible.'

He continued at length to show how the research and development of his Establishment could be integrated with those of industry and universities in general and ended up with a strong point: 'Just in closing, some of you may be thinking that taxpayers' money could well be saved— well, I would just say this. Apart from our primary task of developing equipment, we have carried out or sponsored a number of researches which have been of direct assistance to industry and since the war there have been sales of equipment which we have either designed or had a large share in the development of whose value is several times the total cost of the Establishment for the same period'.

At about the same time as he was giving these sort of talks a nice piece of whimsy was published which must have given him some light relief from the sombre demands of his duties. He received a charming book called *In Doodle Wood*, written for children of all ages by Stephen Galpin. Although published in 1951 by Edmund Ward Ltd, London, it was inscribed by the author '15 October 1957. My dear Donald, I have taken the liberty of including you in this book on page 124 and trust I may be forgiven. With all good wishes. (Signed) Stephen.'

This was a neat and witty description in verse of a beaver building a dam. Here is the relevant extract with its underlying theme of the beaver using 'Bailey' principles:

'Now all things being ready
The Bridge was fit to launch,
And so to keep it steady
He joined two timbers staunch,
Which stretching out like slender snout
Towards the further side
Made a 'Beaver' cantilever
An easy thing to slide.

Pushing bridges from behind
Requires a piece of string
To see that it is all aligned
And straight as anything.
But Donald B. most cleverly
Had calculated right
By markers two, and looking through
His new theodolite.

So working with his lever
Himself as counterweight
Bent double like a heaver
He bridged the roaring spate.
Though I can fly, Oh would that I
Had half his wisdom clear;
I make a mess, and must confess
I am no engineer.

Yes, what a great achiever
Was that little spotted beaver
With his boat, his ram, his lever
And the laws which he obeyed

Yet what a sad deceiver
Was his engineering fever
For the mice all crossed the river
On the bridge which he had made!'

But gradually, despite his successful expansion of the work and importance of MEXE, the cards dealt by fate were stacking up against him.

True he had gone to the USA and Canada in the pursuit of technical
collaboration. His USA counterparts gave him the welcome and hospitality for which they are justly famous as already described. His bridge
was adapted in gigantic scale to assist in Toronto's underground railway.
Over 200,000 tons of Bailey equipment he saw being used for an enormous
hydroelectric project in Ontario. He also inspected 2,000 feet (600 metres)
of his bridge being put up as a temporary replacement for one that had
collapsed. Only a small story in the *News Chronicle* recorded his trip. It
quoted him as saying 'My tour took several weeks and I went pretty well
all over America . . . I was fêted at dinners almost everywhere I went'
he confessed modestly 'until it became really hard work'.

I have brief jottings he made about a trip to India in the mid-1950s,
the purpose of which was to liaise with and to advise the authorities there
on various technical problems. The notes give place-names accompanied
by mysterious cryptic references like 'caste system . . . oxen . . . smells . . .
bath house with scent spray . . . small boys touching feet . . . prophet's
footprint. . . .' But even here he finds room to finish with a bit of humour.
The last two lines are almost full sentences. '*Times of India* cartoon.
Overseer to fire walker 'You have dug a trench one mile deep instead of
one mile long—never mind, get on with it.'

These were but passing interludes between two major events which
disrupted his professional career, and which did much to make him a
very unhappy man. They left him sad and disillusioned. He carried the
bitter memory of them to his grave.

From the outset he was determined to establish the fact that he was
the inventor of the Bailey bridge—a protective impulse which anybody
anywhere who has ever invented anything will readily understand. So
way back on 14 October 1941 he applied for a patent entitled 'Improvements in, and relating to, the construction of bridges and other metal
frame structures'. But for years nothing happened because he was too
busy to pursue it until after the war. In any case there was the traditional
argument he had to face that as a Civil Servant the ownership of the
patent under the terms of his employment was vested in the Ministry of
Supply. In proof of that fact he had to stomach the formal assignment
of the patent he wanted to the Minister on 6 February 1947. To add
insult to injury he then had to watch it being further assigned by the
Minister to another government body, the National Research Development Corporation. It seemed that many were getting their snouts into a

profitable trough except the man who most deserved to be first in the queue.

So by way of getting some formal recognition and compensation for this invention there was only one thing left to do. He made a claim through the 'usual channels' for some financial reward. This hit the bureaucratic brick wall in the same way as his plea for a patent. He was deeply hurt. He could not believe that all his years of sweat and achievement could be so callously disregarded. So he made a very brave decision, particularly for one whose livelihood depended in terms of a salary and above all a pension on not upsetting his employers, the mighty monolithic Ministry. He decided to fight the decision. To quote his own words when he spoke to the Press: 'The Crown has ruled that my invention was part of my ordinary duties as a military bridge builder, and as I was paid for the work, there was no ground for an inventor's claim. So I have decided to fight back and be represented by legal advisers. The fact is that, although my invention eventually took shape in the course of my duties, I had to originate the concept and develop it all in my spare time. It took years to get Ministry and War Office approval. Often when I mentioned it they could not be bothered with it.'

The newspapers took up the story with headlines such as 'Bailey Bridge man to fight "no reward" decision'; 'He invented Bailey bridge at nights'; 'No help—but Bailey built his bridge'; and 'Invention claim by Bailey'.

After a nerve-racking two-day hearing in June 1947 when his case was argued by Mr James Mould on his behalf before members of the Royal Commission on Awards to Inventors under their chairman Lord Justice Cohen (or the Right Hon. the Lord Justice Cohen as he then was), it became clear that behind the niceties of the 'legal-speak' between 'learned friends' no punches were pulled, especially those aimed below the belt. Treasury Counsel based its case on the assumption that Sir Donald, as a Civil Servant attached to the Experimental Bridging Centre, perfected his invention as a matter of duty. Sir Donald's Counsel sought to show that his client was so bound by routine duties and official policy that he was only able to develop his idea in his own time and to press his case when officially blessed projects had failed under test.

Apart from the virtues of the Bailey Bridge—which were admitted by Treasury Counsel—Mr Mould made a point of the invention's patent. 'The whole rights in respect of the invention become the property of the Ministry [of Supply]. *Even the use of the bridge's principle as a toy is controlled by the Ministry*'. (The italics are mine.) He claimed 'it was no part of Mr Bailey's duties as a servant of the War Office [and Ministry of Supply] to make the bridge.' It was 'only his sense of duty that made him override the limitation, imposed by his terms of employment, to use his leisure time perfecting the idea.'

It was established by the Committee that, according to the evidence submitted, all revenue and emoluments from the invention, including post-war developments, were to accrue to the Ministry of Supply. It was further established that Sir Donald's salary, at the time of the invention, had risen from £300 to £549.

That last point about his salary must have given the Treasury Counsels a boost. Fancy Sir Donald being lucky enough to get an increase in salary which brought it miniscule annual increments over quite a number of years from £300 to £549 p.a.! It is a pity they did not see fit to emphasize their generosity by rounding it up to £550 by giving him an extra £1.

In his final address Mr Mould said: 'It is clear that as the result of some work which was done by Sir Donald the bridge got into the hands of the troops at least 12 months earlier than it otherwise would have done.'

However at the end of the day things started to look brighter. Lord Justice Cohen pronounced: 'Having regard to the great value of this invention, is it not a case that, notwithstanding that the invention lay in the scope of his duties, Sir Donald should receive some reward? Sir Donald is entitled to every credit, both morally and I hope financially, for what he has done in his spare time.'

Lord Justice Cohen's sympathetic remarks must have been taken into account. It was revealed in the evidence that as early as 1936 Bailey put up the suggestion for using standardized pre-fabricated units but was refused facilities and was told that he must not work on his invention during official hours. One's mind boggles at the sheer imbecility of those who caused Donald Bailey to despair by outlawing his initiative.

Eventually he was awarded the sum of £12,000 which was less than a quarter of the sum he was hoping for. But much to his consternation the Ministry of Supply calmly deducted £5,400 from it in tax and by the time he had used much of the balance to meet his legal fees, he virtually got nothing. It is difficult to beat the system or whatever one calls the juggernaut of injustice. However, shortly afterwards, doubtless prodded by cries of 'shame' and pangs of what passes for ministerial conscience, the tax was refunded.

An interesting postscript emerged when the *London Evening News* published a short report dated 17 December 1948. It opened with a simple statement in italics which said: 'Two comments by the Royal Commission on Awards to Inventors in a report today.' It then went on to give in two short paragraphs a damning indictment of the way Bailey was treated both in terms of his inadequate recompense and the absence of support he received. The first paragraph was as follows: 'Air Commodore Sir Frank Whittle, pursuing his idea with remarkable tenacity, met with co-operation from the Air Ministry designed to equip him with the best possible scientific background. Sir Frank received £100,000 tax free for his jet engine invention.' The second paragraph said curtly: 'Sir Donald Bailey, who was awarded £12,000 tax free for his "remarkable achievement" of the Bailey Bridge, met with official discouragement and found no official facilities.'

Without detracting in any way from Sir Frank Whittle's marvellous contribution, it is known that the Germans also had developed a jet-plane prototype and some say they were first in the field with this type of propulsion. I mention this just to make the point that Bailey's invention had no competitor. It was unique. There was no similar bridge concept being produced anywhere else in the world.

So one can imagine Bailey's frustration and resentment when on 25 July 1955 the very last claim before the Royal Commission on Awards before it was disbanded suggested in effect that he had stolen his idea for his bridge from others.

It was a claim by Lieutenant General Sir Giffard Le Quesne Martel who contended that his box girder bridge was used by Donald Bailey as the basis for the design of the panels used in the Bailey bridge. Sir Giffard Martel claimed that the Bailey Bridge was a development from two inventions — the Callender Hamilton bridge and his own box girder bridge, using prefabricated sections connected by pin joints at each corner. He said that when he introduced the girder bridge design in 1920 it was hailed as the greatest advance yet made in such design. He sent a long letter to Stair Stewart in June 1955 who by that time was a Brigadier in charge of a big programme of building all types of accommodation for the forces in the Middle East. In it he mentioned the injustice of Donald Bailey's being given all the credit and ended up by saying:

'The reason why I have sent you this long letter is this. I have made it clear from the start that I will not take a monetary award and if any award is made the whole of it will go to the Royal Engineers' Benevolent Fund. As this is an RE matter I cannot see why our corps should not receive the credit and also any award that is made on the score of the Box Girder being the forerunner of the Bailey Bridge. The light box girder was very speedy and handy with its four-pin joint and it seems almost absurd to suggest that this was not the fore-runner of the Bailey. This matter is now being considered at the Ministry. I do not at present know if they will want to have evidence but could you let me know if you are in general agreement with the above, and whether you would then be prepared to give evidence verbally or in writing. The matter may be dealt with quite soon. I am only raising this from the Box Girder aspect and not from my other various inventions.'

Stair Stewart's courteous reply did nothing to support the General's claim. He made it clear that he honestly believed that Martel's bridge had no significant influence on the design of the Bailey which was 'really totally different in character', as he put it.

During the hearing before the Royal Commission on Awards, Donald Bailey stated that he was responsible for modifications of the large box-girder bridge. It was redesigned for larger roads and the span increased. He added: 'Eventually I was a bit fed up with working out other people's ideas and started off on a new type of bridge, working from first principles.'

When I put all this to him years later he answered quite unequivocally: 'Martel's Box Girder Bridge bore no resemblance to my bridge. His was a riveted structure. I should know because I myself was asked to re-design the Martel Bridge and after doing all I could with it I realized it had to be replaced by something completely new—working from first principles.' He wrote to me confirming these facts. Donald Bailey was a very fair man and he would not have done so if he felt that credit for any part of his concept was due elsewhere.

The essence of the claim was that Bailey's concept could not have failed to have been influenced by his familiarity with Martel's bridge in particular and also the Callender-Hamilton bridge. Accordingly the origin of his invention was deemed to be so vested in the evolution of previous designs that not only was his award misplaced, to put it mildly, but should have gone instead to Martel.

Having seen some of the documents underpinning Martel's case I was struck immediately by some puzzling questions. Why, for example, was Martel's claim not heard until 1955, some eight years after Bailey's submission had been approved by the Royal Commission and well public-ized? A revealing sentence written in a paper by one supporting Martel suggested it was due to his modesty. It said: 'The whole of the General's outlook on the war to come, even from when he was a young man, was one of attack, though so modest personally in regard to all he has done that a claim for "war-winning" bridge invention and organization done chiefly in the 1920s is not put forward for serious consideration by his Country till 1955'.

I find it strange that the gap of so many years should be so ascribed, especially as I will show later that questions intended to brief his Counsel were so constructed as to confirm Martel's desire for recognition. It does not seem to add up. Another document indicated that Martel and others had entered claims before the Bailey case was heard but were not asked to attend or even told the hearing was to take place. Strange again that with the publicity it got there appeared to be no knowledge of it, or if so, no protest.

The same writer, emphasizing Martel's many distinctions (unques-tionably he was an outstanding man in many different fields apart from bridging) added these two distasteful observations about Donald Bailey which may have been counter-productive: 'This account [i.e. Martel's] is then a far more interesting story of the real origin of World War II bridging than the Ministry of Information version of a Civil Servant dashing down an inspiration on the back of an envelope after a bridging test. That inspiration would appear to be the utilization of the inspirations already at hand which he was provided with already and instructed to make full use of, following their purchase by the State'.

This remark pouring considerable doubt on Donald Bailey's effort is of the stuff of libel, but the next one is so insulting that one can envisage Bailey fortifying his resentment by filling his pipe with unusual care and studied indifference. 'What is given, of one's best, is never given without sacrifice, and I think that sacrifice was least on the part of Sir Donald Bailey, who was never required to stir from Christchurch for his bridging experiments, and greatest on the part of Sir Giffard Martel who, had he put his efforts and personality to pure military work, might well have been the Allies' greatest General.'

While the undoubted qualities of General Martel may give substance to the writer's enthusiastic speculation, his reference to Bailey is neither true nor fair. How does one quantify sacrifice? They both gave everything for their country, and an outstanding civilian does not have to bow the knee in this respect to an outstanding soldier simply because he had no option in wartime to be anything else but a Civil Servant and to be confined of necessity to his place of work.

But it is in the relentless pursuit of the theme that Bailey would never have invented his bridge had he not already been influenced by his working knowledge of the Martel, Callender-Hamilton, and other bridges, that many questions were constructed. In a list setting out no less than 30 of these, and some of them containing questions within questions, there is the constant suggestion that he was never an inventor, but, by putting previous bridge designs together, he was merely a 'co-ordinator'.

Picking out some of the questions to illustrate the main thrust of the interrogation of Donald Bailey one can sense the heavy sarcasm with which they were laced. 'For some years after you went to the Experimental Bridging Establishment would you say your work was coordinative rather than inventive, or inventive rather than coordinative, or both?'

'I gather you were not influenced, when some years after you had been there you thought of the Bailey bridge, by the Martel Box Girder Bridges and Callender-Hamilton Bridges you had been testing; or I expect by Inglis or Hopkins or other earlier military bridges?'

'Would it be fair to say you stubbed your toes on Martel Box Girders almost whenever you walked out of your office?'

'You saw these bridges, tested them, studied their performance and stability, prepared erection gear for some of them, but they did not influence the Bailey Bridge design?'

These sorts of questions were followed by some hypothetical posers like this one: 'If asked to design an aeroplane, might the shape and propulsive mechanism of some aeroplane you had seen, or flown in, come to your mind, or would you rigorously banish that thought and decide to start afresh with say a wingless device for example so it could be solely yours?'

To follow the line Martel and his advisers were pursuing, there would be a case here on a *reductio ad absurdum* basis for the Wright Brothers, if they were still alive, to nip over to Europe and lodge a claim against Concorde.

The irrelevance of the questioning clutched at a new straw when after mentioning the fact that A.M. Hamilton (of Callender-Hamilton bridge fame, a most distinguished and highly respected engineer of great experience) had left his job in Kurdistan between the wars to press his ideas on the Royal Engineers' Board, it was suggested: 'You did not have to risk much or leave an established job or service owing to a conviction about having better bridging to offer than the Army then possessed?'

This might have been an attempt to try and show that Bailey did not have the courage of conviction of a real inventor. It ignored the fact that Bailey was in the one job from which there was no point in leaving. On the contrary his job put him in pole position, after four years of trying, to get his concept at last accepted.

There were many questions pointing to the similarities of the various components of all the bridges which were angled exclusively to accuse Bailey of palpable plagiarism in his design. But it was all to no avail. Although he emerged professionally unscathed, he was dreadfully upset by it all. He did not say much about it to me, but I learnt from his family that he was deeply hurt, and it left a lasting scar in his mind.

The salient fact was that at a time of catastrophe in 1940 when Britain needed the Bridge nobody, but nobody, came up with the answer except Donald Bailey. His long years of work at the EBE on other bridge design had made him familiar with their shortcomings, and whereas his concept to incorporate of necessity a great deal of the conventional bridging wisdom that had evolved over previous decades, indeed over centuries, he found the final solution to all the new problems. Not only that, with the care and precision of his meticulous planning, aided by his great team at the EBE, he got the bridge into mass production and into active service in the shortest possible time. Invention of ways and means was as much his forte as that which is signified by a patent.

With the benefit of hindsight, long after the Martel case was concluded, an informal but informed review of its merits was made for me in confidence by a number of distinguished engineers with long bridging experience. They were unanimous about the advances and advantages conferred by the Martel and Callender-Hamilton bridges in their time, and in particular were full of respect and praise for the character and qualities of the men after whom these famous bridges were named.

Equally they were unanimous in confirming that Donald Bailey's design by comparison represented such a significant improvement in its simplicity, speed of erection, and versatility, and that he was fully entitled to the recognition he had received. They also pointed out that his idea would have come to the fore much earlier had he not been actively discouraged from pursuing it when he first raised it with his superiors.

It is interesting that General Martel, while not having his claim about Bailey upheld, did in fact get £500 in recognition of his contribution to bridging design between the wars. In the summary presented by the Commission it is interesting to see that the Ministry's parsimonious policy was just as consistently deployed in 1924 as it was against Bailey in 1947.

Martel submitted his bridge design in 1919. He was refused permission to take out a patent but in 1924 he received an award of £200. His type of bridge actually continued in useful service up to 1942 when us it was replaced by the Bailey Bridge.

The final outcome which gave Bailey a further and very unexpected place in history was that in order to obviate future claims by inventors, no further bridges were personalized. So Bailey was the last name to be associated with a military bridge. They now have a complete anonymity such as 'Medium Girder Mark Ten' or whatever.

As if to combat the tedium and frustrations he endured Bailey sought to expand his social obligations. His leisure activities in the 1950s included great personal participation and interest in his golf club, a local museum, the rotary club, Masonic Lodge, and the Tiger Motor Cycle Club. One would think that these interests would more than take up all his time. But no. He was also a Justice of the Peace, he gave support to National Savings Week, and was made the honorary president of several organizations including the local light opera company. This variety of roles must have done much to bring new interest and relaxation in his busy life. As usual the speeches at some of the functions were apt and humorous in his long cultivated and succinct style.

His devotion to the subject in question and light-hearted vein made him a popular speaker. His secret, of course, reflected the same attitude which he adopted in dealing with his technical problems, be they designing, a bridge or even calling a hand at the card game aptly called 'Bridge'. He would work from first principles and then construct with care, as his neat notes revealed, a tailormade speech for each occasion. My reference to the game of bridge was brought to mind as a result of a conversation I had with one who played it with him. He was thoughtful and prudent as befits an engineer in his opening bids, insisting that one should have at least five honour cards before considering a contract.

So we find him in amusing form being instructed by the Worshipful Master of his Lodge to propose the toast to 'The Ladies' at a dinner in their honour in 1953:

'This is Ladies evening and I am not going to take up a lot of their time—it should be one of those evenings where a speech should have a good beginning, a good ending but both should be so close together that I should now be about to sit down! However the opportunity must not be missed to thank them for the way in which they look after us week in, week out. Looking round at brethren gathered here tonight I can see quite a number who are weighty tribute to that care.

'In spite of some improvements in conditions, the housewife has many worries to contend with and surmounts them well. I am reminded of the story of the political speaker who in the course of a somewhat ranting speech declaimed—and what is the housewife's greatest trouble?—swiftly came the answer from a rather bored lady in the front row: "Having too much week left at the end of her money".'

It was when he was nearing retiring age that he was moved in 1962 from MEXE to become Dean of the Royal Military College of Science. This appointment which some deemed to be not much in the way of promotion was his last official one. It carried with it a stipend of £4,000 p.a. plus accommodation at a nominal rent.

His departure from MEXE was not without mixed feelings on all sides. He was a civilian and this was now a *military* establishment although a good number of the several hundred working there happened to be civilians as well. It was inevitable that his long tenure, his supremacy of reputation and his continuance in high office, possibly blocking military promotion, could combine to cause resentment and jealousy among subordinates and loftier echelons of the military old boy network alike. I have no concrete evidence for this, but remarks expressed by a number of the people I met during my research all suggested that there was a growing feeling that Bailey had been there too long.

He admitted to me also that in the early 1960s, while still thoroughly enmeshed in and enjoying his job at MEXE, he began to experience self-doubts and strain. This disquiet can be attributed to two main reasons. He became aware that the increase in MEXE activities, much of which he himself had helped to originate, was now outstripping his personal capacity to deal with in the way he would wish. He also continued to fret about the difficulties he had faced years earlier in getting his famous bridge properly recognized for an award as its inventor, and the sniping at or denigration of the originality of his design which had cropped up later.

He bequeathed to me an amusing speech he made at one of the College functions just six months after joining where once again he was proposing 'The Ladies'. The extract reveals more of his talent for carefully prepared humour to fit the occasion:

'Constant attendance at dinners does tend to play havoc with the figure and I am reminded of the case of the lady who, after attending a college function like this, decided she should check upon the position and came away looking rather glum. "What's the matter" asked her husband, "a little over-weight?" "Not at all" said the lady "but according to the chart on the machine I should be six inches taller".'

But underlying this facade of light-heartedness, the stresses of the years were taking their toll. This was sorely aggravated by the knowledge that his wife Phyllis, to whom he had been married for over 30 years, had contracted cancer in 1961. They had met in the early 1930s in the happy and conventional environment of their local tennis club. They had one son, Richard, born in 1937, whose alleged fondness for playing with a meccano set when he was about six years of age was further alleged in newspapers reports to have inspired his father with ideas for his bridge.

As one can imagine, the Bailey domestic scene was one of considerable strain for all three during and after the war years. The nature of Sir Donald's work, always shrouded in secrecy and engulfed in endless hours of travel and business away from home, left Richard and his mother very much on their own. Richard rarely saw his father except on Sundays and was sent to a boarding school when aged 13 years. When I met him early in 1987 he was a strapping man who, unlike his father, had both a fine head of hair and no desire whatsoever to design bridges. He had carved out his own niche as a lecturer on wild-life conservation at London University.

Sir Donald's retirement from the Royal Military College of Science was hastened by his having a stroke in 1966. He collapsed in the street in the town of Swindon and was rushed to hospital. Urged by his anxious wife and friends he gave up his duties, having reached retiring age anyway. He prepared to settle into a more sedentary and leisurely way of life. He unfortunately continued to have a series of minor strokes and suffered a cruel, if not unexpected blow, when his wife finally succumbed to her cancer after a 10-year gallant fight. She died in 1971. Somehow he managed to keep going. The flesh may have been a bit weak after all this but his spirit was not only willing but undefeated.

However the gradual erosion of his health culminated in his having a further stroke in 1975 in Bournemouth. Once again the spirit which enabled him to defy the impossible when he built his bridge came to his aid. Although his speech was impaired and he was partially paralysed he survived. He valued his independence and although offered a home by Richard and his wife Susan when he became a widower, he managed to cope with daily help and with the constant visits and care of his sister-in-law Miss Joyce Andrew.

But as medical experience often confirms, when someone has had a stroke his or her personality can change dramatically. Richard confided to me that, while up to then his father had always been kind and considerate to others, after his stroke he became sometimes irascible and difficult.

Being puzzled by the incidence of these strokes I wondered what caused them. When one reflects that he had led an active, productive, and distinguished life, it would seem that no reason should or could be found there. Furthermore when one reflects that he was of good physique, never obese, slender of frame, played golf, and often rode his bicycle, it was not lack of exercise nor any physical pressure on the heart which was the cause. In conversation with Richard I put it to him that there must be a bit of a mystery about it, and could he help? His immediate response was 'There is no doubt about it in my mind. It was my father's posting to the Royal Military College of Science which brought it all on'. We talked about it, and Richard told me that on visits to the local pub in Shrivenham for a drink with his father, the trouble and stress which his father was experiencing in his role as Dean came out in their conversation.

'He was like a fish out of water' said Richard, who recalled incidents reflecting his father's unhappiness. On one occasion he came home from the College at 4.30 p.m. and his wife, Phyllis, taken by surprise at this unexpected variation of his lifestyle, enquired solicitously 'What's the matter, aren't you feeling well?' He replied gloomily to the effect that everybody had gone home and there was nobody left to do anything. Phyllis was so concerned about her husband's depression that she started to take up golf lessons in the hope of giving him some companionship when he went around the local course playing his favourite game for relaxation.

He was not unpopular with the staff at the College, but the transition at this late stage in his life from his previous high-powered role to a more passive academic one left him stranded. While outwardly serene, inwardly he was unable to cope.

Late in 1977, Richard told me, his father collapsed on the stairs and neither he nor Susan could move him and an ambulance had to be called. Again he recovered and was determined to get out of his nursing home, which Richard explained was just a temporary expedient to provide proper supervision and accommodation as he was out at work and his wife was pregnant. Then fate, which dealt Sir Donald so many unhappy cards, came up with the Ace of Hearts. It is a strange story but one that proves the adage that every cloud, and he had seen many, has a silver lining.

Despite the traumas and trials of his numerous strokes he still had a clear mind and a determination not to be a bother to anyone. So he decided to go back to his bungalow near Bournemouth. As he would need nursing help he asked Richard to place advertisements in *The Lady* magazine which specialized in this form of recruitment. The first replies, vetted by Richard, did not seem suitable, especially one from a man offering his services as a 'housekeeper' which Sir Donald objected to on the grounds that a live-in male might lead to possible misinterpretation. There appeared to be a difficulty in attracting the right kind of applicant but eventually, as a result of an advertisement submitted to *The Lady* by Sir Donald himself, he got a reply which changed his life.

Mrs Mildred Stacey, a widow, had written to him and her letter struck just the right note. He asked her to visit him and an immediate rapport and a happy recognition of mutual compatibility were evident. 'You shouldn't be here. I'm going to get you back home', she said, and I have her own word that she said it. It is a matter of reasonable conjecture

116

that nothing gave him a greater lift since the successful testing of his bridge and the Public Orator's speech when he got his Honorary Degree at his old University, Sheffield.

Anyway, Mrs Stacey got him back and nursed and looked after him for many months. Her constant care and attention had their beneficial effect on his well-being, but then the time came when for her own family reasons she had to leave him. He obtained local assistance on a daily basis which she helped to organize. The parting was not easy as they both had developed an affection and respect for each other. Mrs Stacey, a motherly and conscientious lady of considerable character, was deeply moved by her invalid's dependence upon her and distressed by how the historic role and vicissitudes of his life had left him in his declining years so unremembered and isolated.

During this gap in their relationship, lasting about six months, they were in touch constantly by telephone. Sir Donald kept calling Mrs Stacey to find out what she was doing, where she might be going, and complaining about the 'home helps' whom he had to keep replacing. The piece of wire linking their respective instruments must have been quite hot at times, carrying as it did the heat of their exchanges. Mildred Stacey was not one to submit passively to a harangue, however benevolent.

The day came when she was free to travel again and she arranged to visit Sir Donald for lunch to be preceded by their having morning coffee with Miss Joyce Andrew, his sister-in-law. While the two ladies were in the kitchen Joyce suddenly said to Mildred 'You know, Donald is very fond of you, you both get on so well together, why don't you two get married?' Mildred thought it over. She was a widow. Her own family were grown up and independent. She reciprocated Donald's affection. It would be nice to have a mutual home where companionship could be shared. She replied 'Well, for that to happen I'd have to have a proposal!'

After lunch Donald, without any preamble, said to her 'Well, what do you think about it?' Mildred immediately twigged that this was the proposal which Joyce Andrew had conveyed to her by proxy, so to speak. She smiled and nodded and added 'but I'll have to talk it over with my children first'. This was a formality. So that is how a widow called Mrs Stacey, became Lady Bailey, when they married in 1979.

One of the highlights of their early companionship came on his 80th birthday. He then officiated at the opening of the most original version of his bridge. This was a miniature 1:20 scale replica made into a celebratory iced cake under the strict supervision of Lady Bailey. He cut the first slice at a luncheon party organized by Thomas Storey (Engineers) Ltd, for whom he had acted as a consultant for many years.

Among the documents given to me was a letter from Major John Hathrell, their Managing Director, dated October 1976. It contained such testimony of the respect in which Sir Donald was held that one suspects it gave him the morale boost he needed at that time, as I am sure it was intended to do. Here is the relevant passage: 'I notice from our records that our current agreement with you expires on 31 December 1976. Notwithstanding the fact that your ill health over the past year or so has reduced the level of your activity, I would confirm that we would be delighted to continue with the arrangement for a further period of five years. . . .'

The last two years of Sir Donald's life were tragic. The onset of senility accompanied by brainstorms resulting from recurring embolisms, made him the victim of erratic moods and of behaviour completely at variance with his normal patient and gentle nature. To make things worse Mildred had the ill fortune to have to leave him for a long time while she went into hospital to have an eye operation followed by one on her hip. His condition worsened and he had a fixation about walking, of which his legs were incapable of giving even a semblance. During Mildred's enforced absence an expensive nursing home failed to give him proper attention, but fortunately his final days were alleviated by the care given to him at St. Leonard's Hospital where Mildred, supported on two sticks, managed to visit him.

Sir Donald died in that hospital near Bournemouth on the 4 May 1985. This was almost to the day the 40th year after the end of World War II in Europe during which 2500 of his bridges had been built in North Africa and Italy, over 1500 during the advance through France, Belgium, Holland, and Germany after D-Day, and a large number in the Far Eastern campaign. So many bridges, yet so little understanding about their significance, even to this day.

This is well illustrated by his son Richard talking to me about how, when news of his father's knighthood became known, he was often asked by his school chums and even adults why his father had been so honoured. When he replied 'for the Bailey Bridge' very often this was followed by the question 'Where is the Bailey Bridge?'

On the same subject Richard recalled how his mother took him for a special luncheon à deux in a local restaurant to celebrate the knighthood and a friend of his mother came up to congratulate her, adding 'He could never have done it without you'. This paid undoubted testimony to the support and steadfastness she provided in their home which must have done so much to help him in all his vicissitudes.

Following his death there were only small notices in a few papers, the one notable exception being a lengthy obituary in *The Times* . This gave a detailed account of his appointments and achievements. It revealed that, apart from his famous bridge that bestrode rivers 'like magic', he took a leading and innovative part in devising a variety of bridging equipment, pontoons, cranes, pile-driving rigs, and trailers to transport them. He was a versatile engineer *par excellence*.

In an issue of the magazine *Metal Construction* (a technical magazine published by The Welding Institute) Colonel J. H. Joiner, who served

TELEPHONE, WHITEHALL 9400.

WAR OFFICE,

WHITEHALL,

LONDON, S.W. I.

31 - 3 - 47

Bailey bridging made an immense contribution towards final victory in World War II. As far as my own operations were concerned with the Eighth Army in Italy and with 21 Army Group in N.W. Europe, I could never have maintained the speed and tempo of forward movement without large supplies of Bailey bridging.

Montgomery of Alamein
Field-Marshal
C.I.G.S.

Field Marshal Montgomery's letter of congratulation on the contribution of the Bailey Bridge to final Allied victory. *Bailey Archives*

for 37 years with the Royal Engineers, wrote a long article entitled 'The Bailey Story'. In it he described succinctly and comprehensively the technical complexities and problems of the bridge's design, construction, and mass production. He ended his excellent article by describing Sir Donald as 'a modest, considerate, and courteous man'. That is exactly what I found him to be.

In reporting Sir Donald's death the *Daily Mail* attributed the following remarks to Field Marshal Montgomery 'Without the Bailey bridge we should never have won the war'. In a testimonial written in his own hand dated 31 March 1947 the Field Marshal, obviously responding to a request to help Sir Donald with his submission for an award as the inventor, said in his last sentence: '. . . I could never have maintained the speed and tempo of forward movement without large supplies of Bailey bridging'. Few would deny that if he could not have done that, he would have been hard put to it to advance.

While so many great men, inventions, and events conspired to save us from being defeated, who can doubt, in the light of the facts and Field Marshal Montgomery's own admission, that Donald Bailey made an outstanding individual contribution to victory.

His memorial service took place in the Priory Church, Christchurch, and the address was given appropriately by one who worked closely with him for many years and knew him well, Brigadier H.A.T. Jarrett-Kerr. He and other working colleagues and close friends like Sir Ralph Freeman, Brigadier S.A. Stewart, and Mr. D.M. Delany, provided ample evidence of the humanity and genius of the man. Without going through the tedious process of attribution in each case, the following extracts summarize the sentiments of these men, and of many others who wrote at that time. It is as well to put them on record, lest we forget.

'He had a natural flair for engineering design, particularly in his development of welded structures, of which he was a pioneer. He was such an easy man to work for, never ruffled, always considerate . . . I do not remember a single cross word from him, and when crises occurred he was resolute and unflappable.'

'He had great strength of character, and at times you could see he was hard put to it sometimes to suffer fools gladly . . . but even then he somehow succeeded!'

'Despite the heavy responsibilities that were his lot, and the honours that were bestowed upon him quite rightly, Donald Bailey always remained an unaffected and simple family man, an affectionate husband, father, and grandfather.'

'He was a friendly and approachable man, whether at the Golf Club, or with his cronies around the bar at the King's Arms. He was as happy with a junior draughtsman or a fitter in the workshop as with a General or Minister of the Crown; all felt at ease with him.'

In is inevitable that the requiem for such a man should provoke the warmest sentiments. Nobody is perfect, and yet when one looks for any of the human frailties to which we are assured our flesh is heir, there seem to be no noticeable traits in Donald Bailey's character to confirm their existence during the whole of his working life.

The last sentence of the address given at his memorial service was not only a relevant and happy tribute at the time, but will serve in perpetuity for all generations to come as a reminder of a man who bequeathed not only a shining example of devotion to his duty, but also a Bridge that links the Continents and all mankind for ever.

'Let us all then join with his family in thanking God for him, some of us with memories that endeared him to us — memories of a truly great but humble man, who rightly deserved the honours bestowed upon him, for he served the nation faithfully and well.'

I am happy to report that the story of a Bailey and a bridge is likely to continue. His granddaughter Christina, one of Richard's family of four, is showing a considerable ability to follow in her grandfather's footsteps. She is studying civil engineering at Sheffield University with marked success. A prophetic omen of her prowess was when, aged eleven, she was given 'bridges' as a project at her school. In the same class, given the same project, was a boy who was the direct descendant of one of Sir Donald's heroes, the man who built the world famous Menai Suspension Bridge. The boy's name was Telford.

Finally I have to hazard the observation that while the civilian and Royal Engineer colleagues of Sir Donald Bailey to whom I spoke were the nicest possible people, to extract anything out of them which constituted human interest material about the man himself and his off-duty life was much the same as working on granite with a broken toothpick. As I said before, if you scratch an engineer you don't draw blood. He draws a bridge. As soon as I mentioned to any of them that I was writing about Bailey and his bridge, they could not wait to tell me about the bridge. 'Sir Donald, ah yes, he was a lovely man, but let me tell you about the medium girder bridge designs, the RSJs, the advances in arc welding, the Mark III version of the Inglis rectangular bridge, M.N. and K. bracing, the bottom chord transom fittings, and the quality of manganese-molybdenum alloy steel'. That was the kind of informative precursor to every conversation and it took me usually a good half hour and an expensive deployment of alcohol to reduce them to my own level.

Normally one would be tempted to say that the death of Sir Donald would be the appropriate end to the story, but in fact this is not so. The story, as the next chapter explains, is likely to go on for ever. The name of Bailey is to bridges what Verdi is to opera or Milton to poetry. The genius of his work bears comparison with any great work, even though it is composed in the language which only engineers understand. Sir Ralph Freeman, when making an explanatory doodle for me about a bridge on a small piece of paper, remarked 'drawing sketches is the way engineers communicate their ideas to each other'. Thinking about it afterwards I decided he must be right. Leonardo da Vinci did it very well.

13 'Let Us Think We Build For Ever'

SINCE prehistoric times there have always been bridges of some sort serving the needs of the community. The permanence of the bridges, many so graceful and of such reassuring solidity, is taken for granted as they span not only small and mighty rivers but also the centuries, and generations of people.

So it was with some amazement that I realized what a paradox the Bailey had become. This structure, designed as a temporary expedient to replace a broken bridge, has become the most permanent and widely used bridge the world has ever known. It is a staggering story. One cannot claim that a single Bailey Bridge in any one location will last for ever, indeed none of the purpose-built bridges can be expected to do that. But it is a fact that the Bailey, which was built in large numbers over 40 years ago, can still be seen in countless countries today; and with some refinements it is still being built.

When World War II ended, the Bailey, far from being demobilized, was pressed into more active service. In the autumn of 1944 it was planned to build what were to be called semi-permanent structures (abbreviated to 'SP' in the vocabulary of that time) and an SP bridge headquarters was set up under prestigious command. This mushroomed into a large private army packed with Brigadiers, liaison officers, technical and other subordinate officers, and a host of other ranks with attendant orderlies, clerks, and vehicles. The single object of this organization, illustrating Parkinson's Law that the work force will expand to fill the room available—and Germany is a big country—was to design, procure, and erect two main fixed bridges across the Rhine as soon as practicable after the Allies had crossed it.

As one knows, a committee can often fall between stools with conflicts of opinions and in this case they designed two kinds of fixed bridge which seemed to be considerably in competition with each other. They both used the Bailey equipment for the superstructure but supported it in one case by clusters of stronger steel piles. But the point of the story is not revealed by this simple technical divergence.

The energies of this high-powered and resourceful committee were allowed to explode in an orgy of planning and also in the preparation, manufacture, and accumulation of vast stores for these bridges in the winter of 1944–45. Factories, particularly in newly liberated Belgium, were requisitioned everywhere. The effort was prodigious. But there was one snag the committee had not catered for. These bridges were meant primarily to sustain the traffic supplying the Allied armies as they advanced. But suppose peace broke out? What would happen then? Would these bridges meet the new conditions?

In the event, hostilities ceased about eight weeks after the Rhine was first crossed by Bailey Pontoon Bridges. By this time the two 'SP' bridges were barely finished. They had taken about six weeks to put together. It has to be said that the Americans took just over ten days to build a corresponding bridge of some 2000 feet (600 metres), more than half of which crossed one of Europe's major waterways with a current running at three to four knots.

When the war ended there was a most pressing need to reconstruct peace-time communications with emphasis not only on road and rail but above all on the river traffic of the Rhine and its associated tributaries and canals. It was quickly decided that the sites of the two British 'SP' bridges, being a long way from the main population centres, were not suitable. Furthermore bridges were now needed to be ice-proof and to have navigation openings wide and high enough for the vital river traffic for which the Rhine, that great commercial artery, was renowned and on which the economy of Germany so much depended. The new bridges were destined for Wesel and Cologne and the SP bridge committee faded out.

One dwells on this post-war episode because the permanence of the Bailey contribution, and its central role in assuring its future in seeming perpetuity, were confirmed. It was the Bailey, in fact, with the inspiration of two brilliant Royal Engineer officers, which supplied the two bridges which once again united Europe as we know it today.

This was an immediate post-war feat almost forgotten except by those intimately concerned and with long memories. It was without reservation one of the most significant contributions which restored the economic lifeblood of the adjoining nations. It provided the platform on which Western Europe built the prosperity it had enjoyed ever since.

It was a mammoth task because the mighty Rhine, the great waterway of western Europe, was blocked in the British zone alone by the desolate debris of no less than 17 road and rail bridges. If France, Germany,

Belgium, Holland, and Luxembourg were even to start to attend to the repair of their economies, the Rhine would have to be cleared and at least one, but preferably two, ice-proof, high-level, and navigable bridges would have to be built before the end of the winter. This was decided by the British Army's Engineer-in-Chief in the summer of 1945 so there were less than nine months to achieve the impossible.

He picked the right man for the job. He was Colonel Kenneth Osborne, DSO, OBE, MC, who was given a new command known as 14th Army Group Royal Engineers (abbreviated to 14 AGRE) which had the distinction of having no troops of its own. Its purpose was to be an umbrella for the many sapper units to which were added vast numbers of civilian workers to carry out a major job. At the age of 30, Colonel Osborne found himself directing some 10,000 men in a race against the oldest of enemies—time.

The man with most say in the design of the bridges was the other officer of the Royal Engineers, then Major Ralph Freeman. He had been seconded in June 1944 to advise the Allied armies in all sorts of tricky bridging operations. At this stage in July 1945, he was an admirable choice because he was already devising a high-level floating Bailey bridge to cross the Rhine at Dusseldorf. This was rightly named the Freeman Bridge about which more will be said later.

Osborne was, and still is at the time of writing, a remarkable character. He had no great formal technical qualifications but he had something a lot better. He had leadership, style, and the ability to get the best out of his staff and work force with ruthless and continuous pursuit of purpose. A shy man, somewhat short of stature Osborne was destined before the war to qualify as a quantity surveyor: he could not have foreseen how his fortune would change.

Having volunteered for a Territorial Army engineering unit before the war started, he found himself in action earlier than most. He got his MC at Dunkirk. This was followed by years of distinguished service in North Africa and Italy where he won his other decorations. Educated in the hard school of constant combat conditions, refined by diplomatic brushes with his Russian counterpart when they met on the borders of their respective zones in Germany, he emerged with the equivalent of first-class honours.

Wesel, a nightmare town shattered by Montgomery's artillery and aerial bombardment, was the depressing site for the first bridge. However the Americans had bequeathed to them a unique temporary steel and timber bridge (built in a few days, as mentioned earlier) which could be used to support parts of the structure which was to be composed entirely of Bailey Bridge equipment.

It is impossible to convey, in a way which the layman will understand, the incessant problems which the engineers with their construction gangs had to solve. For the first six weeks the existing American bridge was

124

occupied by German pile-driving contractors; and even this facility was curtailed when a 200-foot (60 metre) gap had to be cut to allow for river traffic, which had by now been partially revived, to pass.

The Bailey panels had to be massed as a permanent bridge to carry very heavy traffic over a third of a mile (536 metres) of a tempestuous and moody river. Furthermore the immense tonnage of the traffic had to be carried over at least two openings giving clearance of some 80 yards (70 metres) wide and no less than 30 feet (9 metres) high to meet the requirements of the biggest Rhine barges. To achieve this, and at the same time to minimize the number of ice-proof piers to be built, Ralph Freeman adopted the well-tried civilian system of alternate cantilever and suspended spans for the whole width of the main river crossing. Thus the bridge would span the whole river in six impressive strides.

All through one of the coldest of Decembers, when icy winds numbed mind as well as hands, the work went on 24 hours a day. Artificial moonlight reflected from the sombre clouds by searchlights provided illumination. In the fight against the whiplash of the deep freeze, the sappers were aided by the issue of a special one-piece zip-up over-garment. This saved the life of the one and only man who fell into the river (a testimony to safety disciplines) because the buoyancy it provided kept him afloat long enough for a rescue launch to reach him.

The icy December was followed in January 1946 by the worst flooding of the Rhine for 25 years. Yet it stands as an immortal tribute to Kenneth Osborne and Ralph Freeman and the thousands in their mighty team who performed miracles in the myriad of more humble jobs that the Wesel bridge was still opened on schedule on 5 February. It was named the Montgomery Bridge to which a reference was made in an earlier chapter when the Royal Engineers units involved in its construction were mentioned.

The Cologne bridge was different. It depended more on waterborne operations than at Wesel and the Rhine in full spate was just as unfriendly. The spans permitting navigation in this case were to be fashioned from German military railway-bridge equipment and had to be floated into position on a raft made from four 1,000-ton Rhine barges. The bridge was opened some months later and named after Patton, the 'blood and guts' American General who had been the first to enter Cologne. For the record Ralph Freeman gives the main credit for the design and construction of this bridge, which he did not stay to see completed, to those succeeding him, first Major Alwyn (Johnny) Long and then Major J. C. (Jock) Lamb.

In the interim a two-bridge crossing of the Rhine was still provided because the Freeman Bridge was able to provide the second string to the Wesel. Thus the original objective was achieved. Some interesting points characterized the Freeman Bridge.

He was asked to design and to complete the Dusseldorf bridge with a sense of urgency. The authorities even went so far as to discount the problems which icing might cause in winter. His analysis took account of the facts that plenty of German skilled labour was about, that pontoon and ancillary bridging equipment was abundant and close at hand. Inspired by a high-level structure he had seen in Holland involving a raft made out of Bailey Pontoons he devised a practical floating highway.

Although his bridge could not be ice-proof he made it rapidly dismountable and capable of being towed to safety to a nearby dock. Knowing that a system existed for giving about 72 hours warning of ice coming down the Rhine he calculated correctly that there was sufficient time, given a proper drill, for all this to be done.

His brilliant improvisation was apparently not matched by the intellect of many of his superiors to whom he had to submit his ideas. Starting with a variety of Lieutenant-Colonels and working his way up to at least one Brigadier, he was struck by the apparent difficulty they had in absorbing the obvious and unique features of a *floating* bridge. This is, of course, that so long as it stays afloat it will always maintain the same height above the water (allowing for the traffic load the bridge is designed to carry). They kept asking him how he was going to satisfy the height clearance when the river rose. Conversely they could have asked what he was going to do about the unnecessary height clearance when the river dropped! However when he got to General Eustace Tickell, right at the very top, no such questions arose and he was given immediate support and the go-ahead.

Major Alwyn Long referred to earlier served both with distinction and with rare dedication to bridging, at the Establishment at Christchurch. He was posted there as a young Lieutenant in the Royal Engineers in May 1942. On his retirement 28 years later he made his farewell speech. It included a story which once again brings together the eternal drama and humour of the sapper confronted as always with the problem of getting a tank over water with the help of a bridge.

At one point in his career, Alwyn Long was promoted and had a supporting staff of several officers including a certain Lieutenant Boswell. Soon after the young Lieutenant took up his duties, a message was received that something had gone wrong with some rafting trials and Alwyn Long hastened to investigate. On arrival he was completely mystified. He had heard the cliché about people walking on water, so to speak, but this was ridiculous. Here was young Mr Boswell bringing a new dimension to the miracle. He was seated quite comfortably to all intents and purposes on the surface of the water in the middle of the river. Closer scrutiny revealed that under Mr Boswell was a light tank and under that was a folding boat raft. Furthermore to add another improbable element to the scene, while all the raft crew were soaked to the skin in scrambling ashore, Alwyn Long was mightily impressed with the fact that not only did Mr Boswell keep his head above water but his feet dry as well.

As I write I have to hand some faded photographs of the Wesel and Cologne bridges which were given to me by Donald Bailey. He remarked in his diffident manner 'these illustrate unusual use of my bridge. Under conditions just as exacting in many ways in peacetime as in war, it confirmed its value for the future. I was very pleased.'

In the chaotic period of the immediate post-war months one would expect naturally the Bailey, devised as it was for emergency use, to excel when the whole of Europe was in a real state of emergency. But it was so simple to work with, so versatile, and so fundamentally sound, having been conceived as Sir Donald said as a pristine new development 'working from first principles', that its Golden Age had yet to come.

Hundreds of Bailey bridges met the myriad needs of countries in every continent. Whenever a bridge over any gap, whether it be to carry road or rail, was destroyed or damaged, a Bailey in nearly all cases provided the answer, not just for a year or two but for many years. For example the Wesel and Cologne bridges put over the Rhine in 1946 were only replaced, though still serviceable, to accommodate growing traffic in the late 1950s and early 1960s. Many of the bridges built in France are still in use more than 40 years later. The same is true of those erected in countless other countries.

But what is also staggering is how the Bailey was in demand for vital roles never before conceived in such magnitude as vital support in building dams for hydroelectric schemes, and as gantries. When one thinks about it, if one builds a Bailey Bridge up into the air vertically instead of horizontally, and one encloses the open sides with extra panels, one can easily produce a very strong tower of considerable height. Furthermore by using the same panels and a little ingenuity one can build diagonal supports for the tower to stop it from toppling over.

So it is not surprising that the Bailey equipment was used in this manner as a rocket launcher 100 feet (30 metres) high for the British 'Skylark' programme in Australia in 1957 and 1958. The 'Skylark' projectile was designed to carry a payload of 100–150 lbs (45–70 kg) up to 100 miles (160 kilometres) above the earth's surface. It carried out a number of successful tests and the gantry withstood the vibration splendidly during the lift-off stages.

Bailey equipment was used *en masse* probably on a scale never seen before on one site, for the Hydro Electric Company of Canada. Words cannot describe adequately the mammoth mountain of multi-storey panels, all acting as support towers and bracing columns and providing a steel wickerwork wall of incredible strength. This was not just scaffolding. It was a study in a striking art form, a veritable symphony of steel, composed by ingenious engineers. Close scrutiny of the photographs shows the diverse roles of those simple Bailey panels. Seeing is indeed believing.

In the subsequent post-war years, with new technology and advances in metallurgy, the Bailey went from strength to strength. Even before the end of the war it was widened to cope with the dimensions of multi-wheeled heavy lorries and within a few years a scaled-up version became a Heavy Girder Bridge which could take extreme weights of traffic with a span of up to 100 yards (90 metres).

But now the main thrust of the Bailey development made use of its potential for temporary or permanent civilian bridging. This was exploited by civil engineers world-wide as one of Britain's greatest assets. Its versatility for other purposes such as gantries, towers, support structures, and a wide range of temporary works on large projects was fully recognized. It says a great deal for Donald Bailey's basic concept and the excellent quality of the equipment that to this very day the Bailey Bridge and its modern version enjoy considerable sales all over the world. This is due entirely to an all-British enterprise involving two rival British companies whose activities have been, and still are, very competitive. Their respective achievements are well worth noting. First of all I will mention Thomas Storey (Engineers) Ltd who had exclusive rights to the Bailey for some years before their competitors (Mabey & Johnston Ltd) were also granted the rights to manufacture.

The Thomas Storey company was founded in 1936 and due to its involvement in the production in wartime of the Bailey Bridge it was ultimately granted a licence to manufacture it by Britain's National Research Development Corporation. The wise precaution was then taken of retaining Sir Donald Bailey as a consultant who advised on the improved versions with enthusiasm. This was a role which they sustained for him, even when he was no longer able through his illness to be actively involved, right up to his death. In view of the vicissitudes subsequently facing this Company, that act of respect and humanity speaks volumes for its spirit and character which enabled it to survive a very bad patch and live to see a profitable future.

The firm joined the ACROW Group in 1960 and continued to expand successfully and twice won the prestigious Queen's Award for Export Achievement. Then in 1984 disaster struck. The ACROW Group failed and went into receivership. This was a very bad time for Major John Hathrell, OBE, its Managing Director. What was to become of Storey? Were 40 years of the great Bailey tradition to be broken? Suppose a predator were to take over who would eat up Storey and decimate its staff? Would the sweat and toil and enterprise which made Storey a profit centre for ACROW now count for nothing? Already newspapers were headlining 300 AT FACTORY FACE JOB AXE SHOCK as rumours of bankruptcy forcing redundancies were circulated. The story was true. Hathrell was shaken. Assuming that somebody else would buy the Company, he was prepared to help any who expressed interest in doing so.

Several contenders put in their bids to get Thomas Storey but John Hathrell had sudden inspiration. Secure in the knowledge that he had a loyal and skilled workforce, and that his order books were healthy, he turned round and fought the invaders to a standstill. He himself conceived and led, with the help of his colleagues on the Board, a management buy-out. The newspaper headlines, once so gloomy, now changed their tune. 'MANAGERS ACQUIRE THOMAS STOREY,' 'BAILEY BRIDGE FIRM IS RESCUED,' they proclaimed.

With the help of good financial advice, bank loans, and the sweat of the brow, Hathrell and his team persuaded the receivers to rule in their favour. The sum involved was nearly £5,000,000 and the clinching factor which enabled them to raise this sum and to make the verdict go their way was that they had a proven track record of management expertise and profit. They beat off very serious competition with these invaluable credentials which, at the same time, attracted sympatheic and financial support from major financial institutions. It is worth mentioning that the famous central bank, leaders of the consortium which decided to call in the ACROW receivers, got a very red face. In the words of one reporter the bank was 'anxious to avoid a public pasting'. It was concluded by the same reporter that the moral of the Storey episode was that 'if you are in a small, profitable, and mature portion of a collapsing parent, the odds are stacked somewhat in your favour when it comes to a management buy-out. You are pushing an open door.'

I think John Hathrell would observe that, open door it might have been, but it had to be given a damn great push! Anyway he re-engaged his staff and in less than a year Thomas Storey was making heartening headway with both his cash flow and the continuance of the Bailey tradition.

They invented floating pontoons which incorporated improved Bailey panels and other Bailey bridging equipment. These 'Uniflote' units as they were called acted as rafts for construction projects, drilling rigs, floating cranes, causeways, ferries, and landing stages; in fact they could provide virtually any floating support. The only limit is that of the imagination. To this was added the facility of an all purpose 'pusher' tug which could round up and position the Uniflote rafts like a well-trained sheep dog. Never were Bailey panels so pampered!

Perhaps the most bizarre role played by the Bailey Bridge was in providing a floating platform on the waters of the Albert Dock, Liverpool. The home of the Beatles was an apt setting for a televised pop concert organized by Britain's independent ITV company Granada. In a parody of the hit by Bill Haley and his Comets of the late 1950s the spectacular, featuring a veritable galaxy of rock stars, was called 'Rock Around the Dock'.

Thomas Storey used 48 Uniflote members to form a 300,000 acre (1200 square metre) area together with five lighting towers and staging superstructure, all of which used panels based on the Bailey principles. The panel's versatility could never have been expected to include its appearance in the chart's top ten, so to speak, by assisting with a rock concert.

In 1985 the Bailey Bridge had another exciting chapter added to its glorious history when a gigantic four-span structure over 500 feet (150 metres) long had to be erected to take traffic diverted from a decaying permanent bridge near Merthyr Tydfil in Wales. It represented the highest temporary bridge in Europe at that time with the centre pile reaching 95 feet (30 metres) and accommodating up to 12,000 vehicles every 16-hour day of which 2000 were heavy goods lorries. Thomas Storey were now advertising their successes in many languages. Their latest constructions were supplementing the numerous Bailey Bridges still surviving after more than 40 years' service.

On the other side of the world further testimony to the enduring Bailey was strikingly demonstrated when in the mid-1980s the mighty Demerara River in Guyana was spanned. Because of the depth of the soft silt in the river bottom which prevented fixed piers being sunk, Thomas Storey engineers floated a double lane bridge across it. This reached the incredible length of just under some 6000 feet (about 2 kilometres). It was cunningly constructed to include a high-level segment mid-stream under which light river craft could pass. A brilliant addition were two retractable spans which could be withdrawn when required to leave a clear 100 yard (90 metre) gap for large ships to pass through.

This majestic and beautifully custom-built structure took only a year to complete. Its official opening by the Prime Minister of Guyana was an occasion for great celebration. Not only did he single out Thomas Storey for special mention but the reggae music to which the crowds were gyrating was punctuated by the call for three enormous cheers for the bridge's work force.

While it is right to dwell at some length on the vicissitudes and undoubted achievements of Thomas Storey, it is imperative in equal measure to emphasize the terrific impetus which the arrival of Mabey & Johnston Ltd gave to the advancement of the Bailey when this company came on to the scene in the mid-1960s.

Having visited their Head Office in July 1987 I came to the conclusion that never had such a locale, a small mansion surrounded by fields of flowers and nursery gardens in a quiet rural setting not far from Reading, England, disguised such prolific engineering dynamism. It was as if they had gone out of their way to provide the visitor with a red herring about their singleness of engineering purpose. Actually I should have said 'turtle' instead of herring because a framed certificate on the wall of the entrance hall declared that a Mr Mabey, Grandfather of the Company's Chairman, held a warrant as a purveyor of turtle to Her Majesty Queen Victoria. This somewhat unusual appointment was derived from a Mabey catering establishment in those days which, rather like the original Lloyd's Coffee House, was a focal point for the City elite.

I was welcomed by Mr Charles Forsyth the young General Manager and Chief Designer who introduced me to Mr Bevil Mabey, the Chairman, and as we talked their passion and pride in expanding the use of the Bailey Bridge was more than evident; it was overpowering.

Perhaps it was something to do with the fact that when Mr Bevil Mabey, an officer in the Royal Signals, was demobilized after the war, he noted the large amount of Bailey Panels in stock, and his engineering instincts were aroused. His interest never waned, so when the opportunity came many years later to share the concession for the Bailey, he jumped at the chance.

Perhaps it was something to do with Charles Forsyth, a graduate of Bradford University, who had further training under the benign and wise guidance of Alwyn Long (mentioned earlier). He could not resist, and still cannot resist, thinking up new improvements on the Bailey which he was constantly making more efficient.

Encouraged by his Chairman, it is largely due to him and his team that the Company has ten patents under its belt; a most difficult protection to secure in the engineering world unless the credentials and specifications demonstrate with palpable and unarguable precision the innovative designs.

As an example he modestly, but with justifiable pride, points to the 'Mabey Compact Bridge' which is now established world-wide, and also the 'Mabey Universal' which incorporates a larger panel. These developments of the Bailey concept are claimed to have singular advantages in carrying heavier loads, having increased stability, and faster erection.

All this was well illustrated when a Mabey Compact Bridge now in service in Alberta, Canada, was ordered in early March 1984. It had to cross a giant waterway with three spans of 170 feet (50 metres) each, so the total length of the bridge was 510 feet (155 metres). The vast amount of equipment for this massive bridge was delivered on site in about 28 days on 7 April 1984. Believe it or not, under the supervision of Mabey engineers it was completed on 13 April—finished in only six days! Then the approach roads were completed and traffic, heavy oil lorries, crossed on 30 April—no less than 25 days ahead of schedule. When one thinks of the speed of delivery of the bridging, the speed of erection, and the remarkable saving in man hours and costs to the client, one is prompted to observe that Mabey do not 'get up and go' so much as to arrive before you can say it.

Perhaps the tradition of research and development, the constant search for the better mousetrap, owes much to the company's pedigree. Its origin goes back to its Chepstow works in South Wales in 1849 where the historic Tubular Bridge, made to the then revolutionary advanced design of Isembard Kingdom Brunel for a railway crossing, was built. Such a high standard of workmanship was then achieved that some years later the agent of the South Wales Railway said 'not a sixpence has been

131

expended upon it since its opening'. In fact it was to last for over a hundred years carrying traffic far beyond Brunel's wildest expectations until 1962. In that year the same company was responsible for removing it and replacing it with a modern design provided by the Western Region of British Rail. That pioneer spirit and inexhaustible enthusiasm for tackling new challenges has brought Mabey no less than four Queen's Awards for Export Achievement. A few of the more dramatic examples of their Bailey expertise and Company philosophy will illustrate why these coveted Awards have come to them.

One of their first orders from the USA involved their supplying 350 tons of equipment to build a bridge 550 feet (168 metres) long. They had all this delivered and erected within 28 days of getting the enquiry. For those like myself who find it difficult to imagine what 350 tons represent, perhaps it helps to know that it is the combined weight of 23 modern London double decker buses.

They set another record by shipping and flying tons of equipment for a bridge 120 feet (37 metres) long to the USA which was achieved within five days of receiving the order. Five days from door to door, so to speak, for such a job was a remarkable feat of speed and organization.

They have provided ten 200 foot (60 metre) bridges for Ecuador to combat the disruption caused by earthquakes. In Turkey they achieved a mammoth operation in building many bridges over existing ones in the very difficult terrain of the Taurus mountain range.

Last but not least of the many examples one can mention is an outstanding contribution to American history. Ellis Island, featured in books, films, and TV series, as the immigration gateway to the USA for Europe's 'huddled masses' in the 19th century, is now being refurbished with an accent on leisure and community facilities to take its place as a focal point of American historic heritage. This little island, lying in the shadow of the Statue of Liberty, had to have a bridge joining it to the mainland so that the vast volume of construction traffic could go backwards and forwards with their heavy loads. The bridge had to be capable of taking two lane traffic and sustain the weight of two 60-ton trucks as they passed each other, and span a distance of 1500 feet (457 metres). A tall order, and carrying with it considerable prestige for the winner of the contract. The Mabey organization once again rose to the challenge and won. It was an immense undertaking, and the whole contract was completed within six weeks.

At the time of writing, the concept of the Bailey Bridge, thanks to these two British companies, is still in evidence in over 130 countries of the world. The simple Bailey panel, born on the back of an envelope nearly 50 years ago, knows no peer. Probably no other British invention has maintained such monopoly and continued practicality in its field. There is no reason why, given its ease of construction, its extraordinary versatility, and its continual improvement, it should not go marching on for ever.

There is no better end to the story, and no better epitaph to Donald Bailey, than to repeat the words of Ruskin: 'Therefore when we build, let us think that we build for ever. Let it not be for present delight, nor for present use alone. Let it be such work as our descendants will thank us and say, see, this our fathers did for us.'

Index